psychiatry at the Institute of Psyc... ᵣₐᵥ ₕₑ ary Consultant at the Bethlem Royal and Maudsley Hospitals and at King's College Hospital, and Joint Editor of the Journal of Child Psychology and Psychiatry. His special interests are in childhood hyperkinesis, psychopharmacology, the development of children with neurological illness, and neuropsychiatric conditions in childhood.

O P T I M A

The
HYPERACTIVE
CHILD

A parents' guide

PROFESSOR ERIC TAYLOR

Foreword by
STAN MOULD
Founder and Chairman of LADDER
(Learning, Hyperactivity and Attention Deficit
Disorders Association)

POSITIVE HEALTH GUIDE

© Eric Taylor 1985, 1994

First published in the United Kingdom in 1985
by Martin Dunitz Ltd

This new edition published by Optima in 1994
Reprinted 1995

British Library Cataloguing in Publication Data
Taylor, Eric
The hyperactive child.–(Positive health guide)
1. Hyperactive children
I. Title II. Series
618.92'8589   RJ506.H9

ISBN 0 356 21059 6

Optima
A Division of
Little, Brown and Company (UK)
Brettenham House
Lancaster Place
London WC2E 7EN

Printed and bound
in Great Britain by
The Alden Press, Oxford

Contents

Foreword   vii
Preface   xv
1. What is hyperactivity?   1
2. Recognizing hyperactivity   10
3. Physical causes of hyperactivity   17
4. Hyperactive children at school   34
5. The influences of family relationships   46
6. Using and abusing diets   55
7. Coping with hyperactivity   66
8. Coping with complications   78
9. Treating hyperactivity   88
10. Living with hyperactivity   101
11. Questions and answers   106
Appendix: Research diagnostic criteria   111
Useful addresses   114
Further reading   118
Acknowledgements   119
International drug-name equivalents   120
Index   121

Foreword

Stan Mould
Founder and Chairman of LADDER (Learning, Hyperactivity and Attention Deficit Disorders Association)

In January 1992, my life had been pretty tough for a few years – I was 43, my marriage had broken up almost two years previously, another relationship had broken up nine months beforehand, I was having significant problems at work, and I was drinking heavily and had few friends. Furthermore, my just fourteen-year-old son's school reports had deteriorated to a level where the school and I were seriously concerned. Strangely, the things they were saying about him were echoes of what was said about me – things like 'if only he'd concentrate', 'why can't he sit still', 'he distracts everyone else', 'doesn't he ever listen?' Indeed, they still *were* being said about me.

In an effort to sort something out, I spent a week in Spain 'getting my head together' that month. Along with other books, I took one on food allergies as I suffer from some of these and felt this might be linked with my behaviour and difficulties. One evening, the book fell open accidentally at a page which mentioned 'hyperkinetic syndrome' or 'Attention Deficit Disorder' (ADD).

I idly glanced at the list of symptoms, sat bolt upright and re-read them with a tightness in my chest and my mouth open. This was IT ... or me, my son, and just about all the males in my immediate family. I had never thought of myself as hyperactive, but people used to comment on my incessant movement, 'butterfly mind', inability to concentrate for long, and how I was always 'on the go'. The thing that I really noticed, however, was the 'Attention Deficit' tag that I could identify with. All my life people had told me to pay attention, and that I never finished anything, if I ever got started on it. All the things I criticized my son for.

To be absolutely certain of my suspicions, I went looking for more information and came across a book by a paediatric neurologist from Australia, *The Hidden Handicap* by Dr Gordon Serfontein. Here it was – the first description I had read of ADD, and it was a second revelation. I had no doubt at all that this was the problem that had dogged me all my life and was the reason for my son's difficulties. Typically ADD impulsive, I rang Dr Serfontein in Sydney. We chatted for 20–30 minutes, one of the most significant things I have ever done. The only person he knew of working in the field here in Britain was Professor Eric Taylor, the author of this book. I was up all night, alternately exultant that help seemed available, and in tears as all the hurt, abuse and fears of 43 years flooded back.

Reading the book, I soon realized that my, and the popular, view of 'hyperactivity' was totally wrong. It is far more than that of naughty children who rush around or lie on the floor screaming in supermarkets, or who were seen as lazy and unmotivated in school. The sort of children, so the popular image goes, who have parents who could not manage them effectively, had no sense of how to discipline, and worse still in the eyes of some people, had no idea of how to feed them. Even more importantly, the book told me that it was now known that the disorder could also be present in adults.

I also realized that the dietary/allergy approach I had had no success with for a long time was indeed out of date and appropriate for only a minority of sufferers. I had tried Evening Primrose Oil as well as vitamin, zinc, and other mineral supplements, all to no avail. I now know that the body can absorb only so much extra of these substances before excreting the surplus; I got rid of some very expensive urine!

That was the start of a long road that all parents with a hyperactive/ADD child have to travel. As my GP had not heard of it, I began to cast around for help for Chris and I, finding little knowledge anywhere on the way. I discovered a Canadian book, rang the author, who sent me information on the American set-up and the names of professionals there. I contacted Professor Russell Barkley in America who sent me masses of information, as well as an American support group, CH.A.D.D. (Children and Adults with ADD).

By July I was having serious difficulties at work due to my ADD symptoms, as was my son in school. We had approached the local authority Educational Psychologist who was unaware of the disorder, and despite a privately done educational assessment which had diagnosed ADHD (Attention Deficit Hyperactive Disorder), refused to agree Chris had a problem – the whole process was less than helpful. There seemed to be no help available at all, although there were some fairly sympathetic members of staff.

We knew by then that medication, in conjunction with other help, is often extremely effective in helping children. After eight months, we finally had an appointment with a local doctor who felt Chris was not severe enough to warrant medication, despite his real problems at school, and his by then terrible self-esteem. A few weeks later we located a Harley Street doctor who felt a short trial would be beneficial.

The results were quite astonishing – in the first *week* he had been moved up an English group and got his first ever grade 'A', had a commendation in Maths; he bought files, folders and ringbinders to organize his work, and his handwriting changed so much that I told him off for letting someone else do his homework!

However, no one was able to help me at all. I was still struggling to convince my GP; I had by then lost my job, for reasons which read like a checklist of ADD symptoms, and I decided to visit Professor Barkley's clinic in America. Chris came with me and had his diagnosis confirmed, and I found that I did, indeed, suffer from ADHD.

The relief! I found it an incredibly liberating experience to know that I was *not* deliberately lazy, unmotivated and fickle, but did indeed suffer from a neurological disorder that is relatively common, though largely unrecognized. We later went on to a conference run by CH.A.D.D., where I was able to see the vast support network there is for sufferers in America.

On our return Chris continued to do well in school, but I was still trying to get help. The small supply of Ritalin I had been prescribed in America was rapidly dwindling, and my GP would not prescribe it for me, although he would for my son. I began the second line of medication, anti-depressants, which helped a little. It took eighteen months and the kind help of an eminent psychiatrist before my GP would accept I did indeed have an attention deficit.

So, what does all this mean? It means that the lack of resources available to help people in this country is such that one has sometimes to go to extremes. It took tenacity, doggedness, an extremely thick skin as well as money, to stand ten months of searching. The knowledge that the loss of £28,000 a year was imminent, and that Chris was in awful mental turmoil certainly concentrated my mind. I had told him of my discovery some time beforehand, mentioned that medication could help and asked him his feelings over taking it. I shall never forget his poignant reply – 'Dad, I'll take anything if it just stops the teachers moaning at me all the time.'

I decided that the lack of information and help here could no longer be ignored, and after my return set up LADDER to begin to publicize the disorder, and start to give up-to-date information to parents. Many professionals still lack an awareness of ADD and how it can affect not just children, but all members of a family and even others in contact with a sufferer. I was determined to rectify this, and also make people aware of the much neglected aspect of medication. Having tried dietary means of resolving the problem, I was aware of the danger of investing a great deal of time and effort in something which rarely works, and was determined that parents would have a more effective weapon at their disposal.

What does it really mean to be hyperactive or have an attention deficit disorder? Most parents of a child with the problem can soon tell you! What does it mean for the child, though? Can a youngster who has suffered criticism almost all of his or her life explain what it is really like to be shunned by many of the people that he or she knows? To suffer the constant criticism from parents, teachers, schoolmates and others?

Parents who are doing their best to bring up children can have a difficult time even when circumstances are reasonable. However, problems can really start if the child is overactive, impulsive, distractible; children with these symptoms are also at higher risk of being oppositional. Parents can often find a whole range of difficulties when it comes to finding help for their child. Not least of these has been the lack of parent-based information on the disorder. The few books available have almost all been on a dietary approach now firmly discredited in America. Things are further complicated by the description itself. 'Hyperactivity' only describes one part of the disorder. In America it is called Attention Deficit Disorder (ADD) or ADHD where hyperactivity is present.

The attentional problems are usually apparent to parents and teachers, but the link between hyperactivity and attention seems to be little known among parents in Britain, where the popular image is of noisy, naughty children who refuse to behave, with parents who are unable to control or feed them correctly. Sadly, a number of professionals seem to think the same, and blame the parents or the child for the behaviour problem. Nothing could be further from the truth. Any parent of a child with ADD knows just how hard it is to cope.

Until recently, information on ADD and ADHD was the preserve of a few people involved professionally with the disorder. As information is being passed around between parents, slowly public awareness and knowledge of the disorder is growing, and parents who take an interest in their child's well-being are beginning to ask critical questions.

One of these questions is where and how their child can be helped. Parents realize that far from being a minor 'blip' in childhood, ADD can have far-reaching educational and social effects. Getting help for children with hyperactivity/ADD is difficult, due to the lack of information and public and professional knowledge – be aware that you are on a long road which must be faced with tenacity. Professor Taylor has given advice on what can be done elsewhere in this book, but as one who has travelled this road, let me say the following –

1   The first step is education – read as much as you can about the disorder. This book is an excellent first step. Others are available, and more will follow as the true nature of the disorder becomes better understood. Talk to other parents and

compare notes. There is great relief in finding that someone else has similar problems to you, and that there really are other people in the world who understand your difficulties. Before seeking help, do your homework. Make certain that you know your subject – you will be speaking to professionals who may not be aware of the disorder, and may be defensive.

2 Approach your school for extra help for your child, especially if they are behind in their work or are unfortunate enough to have other problems, such as learning difficulties in reading or writing. Ask the school to arrange for the local educational psychologist to carry out an assessment. Show them this book! Take as much literature as possible and discuss it with the teachers. All schools should have a teacher responsible for children with special needs; be aware that some may not have heard of the disorder, so be persuasive, not antagonistic. Get the free booklet from the Department of Education 'Children with Special Needs'. This explains your rights under the Parents' Charter.

3 Approach your doctor for assistance. Ask him what the local facilities are – most hospitals have a Child Development Centre or similar. Ask to be referred there. Get a copy of the Patients' Charter from the Department of Health. You may wish to have a trial of medication, but be aware there is a different attitude to medication in this country, so you may find some opposition from doctors who have never prescribed it. Most only pre-scribe in extreme cases. This is understandable, but if you are offered medication, I urge to you have a short trial. All children deserve an opportunity to succeed at least once.

4 There may be various psychological services available such as family therapy, behavioural therapy, training in social skills, cognitive (thinking) skills, and some children with motor control problems may benefit from occupational therapy exercises. Don't think of it as being a failure if you need this help – think of it being like the top mechanic in a garage who needs specialist training because he only services the special cars. Become a wise consumer and find out the services available in your area, and take them if offered. Temper this with the knowledge that an individual service will not 'cure' the problem, but may help alleviate a symptom.

5 I believe that parent education is one of the most important factors. It is the parents' responsibility to bring up their children effectively, and if a child is hyperactive/ADD that task will be all the more difficult. Find out as much as you can on how to bring up children – being a good parent is not a God-given skill, and some of us are worse than others. As ADD is hereditary, there can often be an ADD parent in the family as well. This makes life doubly difficult, as the ADD parent will often be irritable, impatient, and autocratic. However, bringing up children is a joint task, and learning about their own difficulties can often help parents become better. Also be aware that there are a number of conflicting views about the disorder. Be careful of the psycho-babble that is sometimes heard. Remember that this disorder is not caused by diet, bad parenting, earth rays, poor quality water or other such claptrap. It is a neurological disorder that has many different effects on people's lives which interplay with each other.

6 Finally, the trail of getting help can be lonely and daunting; one is often faced with hostility and scepticism. One of the most important steps to take is to join a support organization. LADDER was formed because there just was no effective support anywhere. I used to phone contacts in America and Australia for help and advice! I hope that LADDER will become a major force in helping parents to gain help for their children. The disorder is complex and wrapped in many myths. Much of these have been disposed of, although parents need to be wary of 'fringe' approaches, often only available privately, and at considerable cost. We are aware of these and can advise parents of the most effective approaches and alert them to those not considered effective.

I am adamant that LADDER remains an Association which is firmly medico/scientifically based, and that we only endorse help for sufferers that has a sound and proven background. Sadly, resources for hyperactivity/ADHD sufferers are few and far between. Compared to America and Australia, we are impoverished in this area; the 'multi-modal' (medical, psychological and educational) approach which works best is not available except in a very few specialist centres. Educationally, many parents see the

Statementing process as a barrier towards getting help for their children. There does seem to be a reluctance to recognize the educational problems sufferers of the disorder can have.

We exist to provide information, education, support and advice for member families going through an extremely difficult time. We know of the few specialist centres providing assistance for sufferers, can provide booklists, copies of articles and literature, and put families in touch with each other locally. We hope to hold conferences for parents and professionals. We have a 'top-down' and 'bottom-up' approach to spreading the word about ADD. 'Top-down' by publicizing the problem with professionals, and 'bottom-up' through parents. As more and more parents request local services for their children, and professionals become aware of the demand, so resources should become available, but it is communal parent power that will force the pace.

Let me make one last statement, from my heart, and as a sufferer of 44 years.

Children have no choice in being born. They have no choice over whether they will be 6 feet or 5 feet tall, brown- or blue-eyed, slim or fat, male or female. Neither do they have a choice whether they will have ADD or not. If they are, they are going to have a tough time in their lives. They will appear perfectly normal, but their behaviour, activity level and attentional problems are going to cause many difficulties for them during their life. If undiagnosed and untreated, ADD kids have a far higher chance of even more severe problems in later life.

Bringing up an ADHD child is challenging, to say the least. When things get tough, reach for the phone and call LADDER, but when you do, remember that your child did not ask to be born this way. Children with ADD are criticized and reproached far more than others, and coupled with the poor self-image that seems inherent with ADD, it does not take many years of this for a child's self-esteem to be destroyed. You are all they have in the world, so even when you feel least like it, *please*, understand them, support them, and above all, love them.

Preface

I have written this book because so many parents of hyperactive children have been confused by the information available to them. 'Hyperactivity' has become a controversial word and this makes some people alarmed, and some suspicious. I work as part of a child psychiatric team that has tried to help a number of children with this kind of problem. This has made me realize how difficult it is for parents when they get conflicting and excited advice from different quarters. It has also brought home to me how complicated the problem can be, and that a lot of the controversy arises simply because one small piece of the truth is present as though it were the whole.

If you listen to one expert, hyperactivity is all a matter of wrong diet. If you listen to another, you will hear that drug treatment is virtually the whole answer. Yet another will tell you that there is no such problem. It is not surprising that parents feel uncertain about which way to turn.

There has now been a good deal of research into hyperactivity, and the problem is becoming better understood. I have known several children whose difficulties have been helped greatly by some understanding education and treatment; and many children who have battled through to happy useful lives. One of the things that has impressed me is how very helpful parents, other family members and teachers can be. A positive, encouraging and accepting attitude can make a big difference to whether children accept themselves and mature out of their problems.

Obviously, however, if you are going to be helpful to your child in this way then you need information. I have attempted to give some in this book. There are some suggestions about self-help steps that you can take, and there are accounts of what is known about the condition. I have tried to indicate some of the limits of knowledge too, because you need to know this as well to help you make decisions on behalf of your child.

I have quite often written of a child as 'he'. I don't mean to imply that affected girls do not matter, or that only boys get it. It is only a matter of style: 'he or she' and 'they' become rather cumbersome after a while. I chose 'he' because hyperactivity is commoner in boys; but both sexes can develop the problem.

1

What is hyperactivity?

This book is written primarily for the parents of those children who show, or are thought to show, the behaviour problems of hyperactivity.

If you are in this position, then you may well already have encountered a good deal of conflicting and confusing advice. Professionals in clinics, scientists and writers in newspapers and magazines tend to disagree among themselves. Much of this stems simply from the unfortunate fact that the word 'hyperactivity' actually means different things to different people. I shall deal with some of the different behaviour patterns in the next chapter. But here I shall be concerned chiefly with what the word ought to mean.

What does 'hyperactivity' mean?

Hyperactivity is a pattern of very restless, inattentive and impulsive behaviour. Hyperactive children are always on the go. They do not relax even when they are in situations, such as in the classroom, that call for relative calm. They do not settle down to games or toys as well as other children of their age, but flit from one thing to another. This means that they tend not to get as much as they should out of their activities.

At the extreme, they may be completely unable to occupy themselves happily. They seem to be searching endlessly for something exciting that never arrives. Hyperactivity also implies a lack of self-control – jumping recklessly to conclusions without thinking about what is involved, and often getting into disciplinary trouble or having accidents as a result.

In other words, hyperactivity means a good deal more than just being very active. Your bright, vigorous child may well be bursting with energy and move around a great deal. This kind of abundant energy may well be difficult to live with but it does not mean that there is anything wrong with your child's development. The distinction between being active and being hyperactive is really one of organization.

If your very active child can nevertheless concentrate well on things that he or she enjoys and can calm down when it is really necessary, then there is no need to think in terms of a psychological problem. The idea of hyperactivity should only arise when your child's activity is chaotic and poorly directed, as well as being great in quantity.

Is hyperactivity an illness?

Hyperactivity is not necessarily an illness. It can certainly be a problem, and when it is severe it can have a major impact on your child's life. However, it is best thought of as a behaviour pattern.

Behaviour is not just a reflection of what we, as individuals, are like, but it is also the result of the situations we find ourselves in. Nearly all children can become fidgety, restless and careless when they are bored or under stress. For example, a teacher may sometimes lose control of his or her class and several children will act in a very noisy and disruptive way. Obviously this does not mean that they have all suddenly developed a disease! This is a glaring example of an understandable reaction to a difficult situation, but sometimes the stresses acting on your child are much less obvious because they are long-term. In such cases, it can be dangerous to diagnose your child as having a medical condition. That would mean that the real stresses might then go unrecognized and untreated.

Nevertheless, severe hyperactivity can be a medical problem that needs treatment and help – and all too often does not get it. If your child appears to be very inattentive and chaotic all the time, in every situation that he or she encounters, then there needs to be a careful assessment. This pattern often starts in very early life, it becomes a particular trouble after starting at school, it may persist for many years and affect relationships, learning and happiness. This pattern is sometimes called 'hyperkinetic syndrome'. It is an invisible handicap, and not the fault of the child or the parents. Research is uncovering the causes, and there are already some treatments that help to keep it under control. The way that researchers, and many clinicians, make the diagnosis is set out in the Appendix at the back of this book.

Arguments over terms

Confusingly, 'hyperactivity' is a word that is used in different ways. Some people use it to imply that they're talking about a case of hyperkinetic syndrome; others use it as a way of describing any kind of high activity in children. This can lead to disagreements between parents and professionals. For example, you could be needlessly alarmed if someone described your child as hyperactive referring only to his level of activity at the time. If you previously understood hyperactivity to be a handicap you might fear the problem to be much more serious than was intended.

The opposite also happens. Sometimes you may feel frustrated if it seems your worry about your child's hyperactivity is dismissed by your doctor or psychologist. The professional may mean that your child has no physical or mental problems and does not show the hyperkinetic syndrome; you may then feel that a behaviour problem has not been recognized.

I sometimes wish that the word could be abolished, because it leads to so many problems in communication. However, it has been used so widely that we are probably stuck with it. In this book I will use the terms:

- 'High activity' and 'overactivity' to refer simply to moving about a great deal, which is not in itself a problem at all.
- 'Hyperactivity' will mean a lasting pattern of inattentive and chaotic overactivity. It can be a problem, depending on its severity and the way that other people react to it.
- 'Hyperkinetic syndrome' will mean a severe and generalized form of hyperactivity that often goes with other kinds of delays in psychological development, such as clumsiness and speech delay.

Other words that are sometimes used

A variety of technical terms have been used in ways that overlap with 'hyperactivity', and these too can be confusing.

Minimal brain dysfunction, minimal brain damage, and **MBD** have all been used as a description of hyperactivity and of difficulties in learning. These are misleading terms because they imply that hyperactivity is always the result of an illness affecting the brain; and this is now known to be untrue.

Attention deficit disorder has replaced the idea of 'MBD' in North America and it has the advantage of not specifying the cause: because there are many causes, each child has to be examined and investigated individually. Attention deficit (i.e. short attention span, distractibility, failure of application) is one part of the complex of problems making up the hyperkinetic disorder. Children with attention deficit may or may not be hyperactive as well. Sometimes a child may seem to be very inattentive because they are preoccupied with worries, or because they are being asked to do work that is too difficult for them – so it is not a single psychiatric disorder.

Learning disorder refers to a problem in learning at school, such as an inability to learn to read. This is separate from hyperactivity, but children with hyperactivity can also have learning disabilities and vice versa.

Conduct disorder refers to antisocial or aggressive behaviour. Like a learning disorder, it is different from hyperactivity, but is sometimes present at the same time.

How do hyperactive children feel?

Children do not usually complain themselves about hyperactivity. Sometimes a bright or introspective child will work out his own difficulties well enough to say 'I can't concentrate on things'; but this is too sophisticated a way of thinking for many children. Usually, children clearly perceive, and suffer from, the reactions of others.

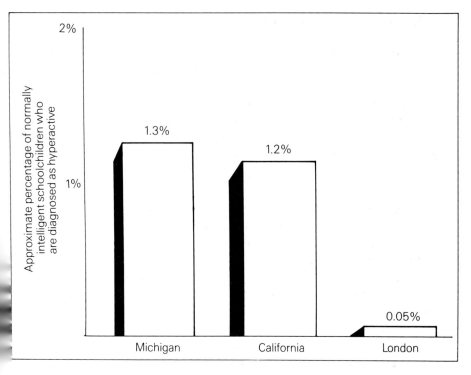

This chart shows the large differences between the number of children diagnosed as hyperactive in the United States and Great Britain. The numbers reflect the different standards for recognizing hyperactivity, not necessarily a higher incidence figure.

'I'm always in trouble'; 'people are always yelling at me'; 'teachers aren't fair'; 'I can't do my lessons' are all representative remarks. They all bear witness to how adults and children have reacted.

Growing up in this atmosphere can be a punishing experience. Some children become angry and retaliate; some go on to think of themselves in very negative ways. They describe themselves in phrases such as 'I'm stupid', 'I'm rubbish', or 'I don't care'. Small wonder that many become alienated from family, teachers and friends; or that frustration and loneliness make many become antisocial and a few act desperately.

Some children, particularly in countries where hyperactivity is diagnosed very often, can come to think of themselves as having 'minimal brain damage' or 'an attention deficit', in a way that gives them an alibi for whatever they do. That can reduce their sense of responsibility for themselves.

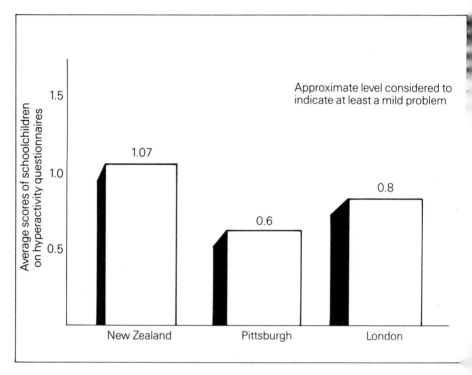

Despite the big differences shown in the previous chart, when teachers were asked to fill in questionnaires, the level of hyperactivity in schoolaged children world-wide was very similar.

The children with hyperactivity who cope most realistically are those who have found that their parents and teachers can understand the presence of the subtle handicap, yet also accept and respect the personality of the child who owns it.

The radical view: hyperactivity as a myth

Hyperactivity has sometimes been oversold as an idea. In some countries whole industries have grown up around it, and especially around the medical treatment with drugs. This has understandably provoked a backlash, a radical critique of the whole idea, and a great deal of public concern.

The essence of this 'anti-psychiatry' case is that hyperactivity is not a child problem at all. The problem lies with adults who like to blame children for the social ills to which they are subject. It is more convenient to label a boy as hyperactive than to try to put right the defects of the school that has taught him badly or the family that has made him a scapegoat.

Whether the 'treatment' is with drugs, psychotherapy or special education, it is still forcing children to change. The correct course of action on this theory, is to change the environment so that it is suited to your child – not to alter your child to fit in with society.

Some aspects of this argument contain a lot of sense. A narrowly medical view claiming hyperactivity is a disease is incorrect if it is applied very widely, and could lead to excessive treatment with drugs and so on. The radicals have clearly described this trap and how it is important to avoid it. However, there is an opposite danger that also needs to be avoided.

It is quite possible for people to close their eyes to the need to recognize when children's psychological development is being held back by severe, disorganized hyperactivity; or to preach wide social reform and neglect an individual's plight. Some hyperactive children, especially the most severely affected, have a problem which would handicap them in any kind of environment. They deserve understanding and help; you, as parents, are likely to find that you have to provide most of it yourselves.

How common is hyperactivity?

Researchers in several countries have questioned children or parents at random to find out how common behaviour problems are. When parents are asked, in effect, 'is your child overactive?' about 30 per cent answer 'yes'. This should be a reassuring figure. It emphasizes that most normal children are very active; and that parents who find it hard to keep up are in good company. Of course, it does not mean that 30 per cent of children have a psychological disorder. In fact, it implies that most children who are thought by an adult to be overactive do not need diagnosis or treatment at all.

Some research studies have asked teachers or parents to fill in questionnaires about the individual behaviours that make up the pattern of hyperactivity. This showed chiefly that there was a big range of activity in schoolchildren. 'Normal' activity is part of this spectrum and it gradually shades into excessive levels at one end.

It is rather arbitrary just where one should draw the line dividing between high normal and abnormal restlessness. There is an argument for being rather conservative about it. Studies in Britain suggest that about one child in 200 has a hyperkinetic disorder; North American researchers suggest that something like 5 per cent to 8 per cent of children have an attention deficit disorder. The difference is not because it is much commoner in North America but because the standards for recognizing it are different.

Naturally, not all the children identified by surveys would be diagnosed or treated. In the United States, research suggests that rather more than 1 in 100 of normally intelligent children in primary school are diagnosed as hyperactive. Most of them are treated with drugs, especially stimulants; for example, amphetamine and methylphenidate (see page 91). This seems too high a figure to most British clinics. In Britain, the figure is more like 1 child in 2,000. British children do get treated for behaviour problems, and in numbers similar to those in the United States, but they are usually given a different diagnosis, often 'conduct disorder'. Furthermore, the stimulant drugs used in the United States are seldom prescribed in Britain. Psychological and educational approaches are more favoured in Britain, but the need exceeds the supply.

Diagnosis and treatment

The best methods for the diagnosis and treatment of hyperactivity are still highly controversial. The truth will probably turn out to lie somewhere between the extremes. But the argument should not be allowed to obscure existing agreement. On both sides of the Atlantic, hyperactivity is regarded as a significant behaviour problem that is different from aggression or bad behaviour. In most countries it is seen as having many different causes, both psychological and physical, some of them inherited and some of them environmental. In most parts of the world, hyperactivity is seen as a risk to psychological development, and there is a real concern to help improve its outcome.

Many people say that hyperactivity is becoming more common; some even insist that there is an epidemic afflicting our children. I do not think that there is any truth in this. It is quite true that more children have been diagnosed as hyperactive over the last thirty years in the United States. This simply reflects the increasing concern about it, and the increasing readiness of paediatricians and child psychiatrists to diagnose it. Young people in Western societies probably have become more lawless over this period – but this is probably a result of social and cultural change, not a specific rise in an illness of hyperactivity.

Complications of hyperactivity

Chapter nine will expand on the question of what happens to hyperactive children as they get older. But, the point to stress at this stage is that much of the importance of hyperactivity is its power to put children at risk of suffering from other problems. Hyperactive children do not usually suffer from the same level of hyperactivity throughout childhood. Usually the original problem is substantially better by the time they reach adolescence.

What is more worrying is that they are vulnerable to failing at school, to developing a very poor image of themselves, and to falling into punishing and damaging relationships with the people who are closest to them. These are the scars that may result from their difficulties in childhood. They can constitute one of the routes into delinquency and even into the adult patterns of problem behaviour called 'personality disorders'. However, the scars are by no means inevitable and their consequences need not be so bleak.

In later chapters I will describe the kinds of treatment that are given. Their long-term goal is largely to prevent the later complications. It is important to remember that most hyperactive children, even without specific treatment, grow up into normal adults.

2

Recognizing hyperactivity

It might seem from the first chapter that hyperactivity is a very easy thing to recognize; and, in a sense, it is, especially when it is marked enough to be obvious, and when it is a rather 'pure' problem, unaccompanied by other kinds of psychiatric disorder. This kind of difficulty is often the easiest type to help.

Hyperactive – or a troublemaker?

Betty was suspended from school at the age of seven. Her teachers said that she was friendly and cheerful, but made the classroom impossible for anybody else. Her loud singing, constant chatter and dashing about disrupted other children; her own progress was held up because she could not or would not settle to any one thing. Her teachers tried in several ways to help her to begin with numbers and reading, but she made no progress in spite of seeming articulate and intelligent.

Other children disliked her and thought she was silly, so she had no friends: but she kept on being very over friendly and bossy towards the others. She was tested by a psychologist, which in itself was difficult because she was so distractible. Nevertheless, when an adult kept her on a single puzzle she could do it very well, and scored above the average on an IQ test (see chart on page 41).

Several kinds of diet were tried at home. All of them worked for a few days when started, but none of them had any lasting effects. Her parents and brothers always found her to be boisterous, full of pranks, and rather self-centred: but had been able to manage well until her education started to go wrong: then her mother became very wretched and started to blame herself for all Betty's problems. However, both parents had been able to be tolerant with little matters and firm with big ones, and had probably helped to prevent her from becoming more emotionally distressed than she was.

Treatment began a few months later. Betty started part-time in a small special class; the teacher broke down learning into small, attainable steps that could be done quickly. Betty attended the clinic to learn self-control techniques, and her parents learned how to help her to practise them and to reward her successes. Her increasing self-confidence helped her to cope with a regular class again, in a different school, and there she made friends happily. She is still something of a tomboy. But she can learn, and cope with the teachers' expectations in terms of discipline, and be popular.

It was important for Betty that her problems were recognized and helped. As a label, 'hyperactivity' seemed to be substantially more helpful than her previous label of 'troublemaker'. Sometimes, hyperactivity isn't really the problem. Chapter five will mention some of the reasons that can lead parents to worry unduly about the possibility. It does no good for a normal child to be given this label – it may even do harm.

Hyperactive – or a sleep problem?

Victor was three years old when his mother, at breaking point, took him to their doctor because she could not cope with his hyperactivity. In fact there was no problem in the daytime. He was a strong-willed, intelligent little boy, and got very cross if he did not get his own way. This was not creating any difficulty for family life, but at night, his mother had had to struggle to keep from hurting him. After a few hours' sleep in the evening, he started a round of screaming after his parents went to bed; he came into their room, threw tantrums when his mother asked him to go back, and climbed into bed with them where he kicked all night.

His mother felt he was so extreme that he must be suffering from a medical condition. Her fear had been intensified by magazine articles about hyperactivity, and by her own lack of sleep. She was also afraid her son would choke himself in a temper if she persisted. Her husband confined himself to making caustic comments on her inability to cope with 'her' son.

In this instance there was really no question that Victor was suffering from hyperkinetic syndrome. His development was progressing well. He showed a common, 'normal' problem with his sleeping; but it had a major impact upon other people. The label of hyperactivity was doing more harm than good because it prevented his parents from responding naturally to a natural difficulty. The way out of this particular deadlock, as I describe in Chapter eight, was personal rather than medical.

Other examples of mistaken labelling

Your child may have a quite different sort of problem that still makes him very active or lacking in concentration. One boy was referred to me because he was overactive. It turned out that he was very anxious about stresses in his home life, and that his anxiety showed itself in a compulsion to touch each part of the room in order. Naturally this made him overactive but not hyperactive.

Children have sometimes been referred to specialists because they find it hard to concentrate; but their main disability is, in fact, a specific learning disorder (see page 40). In most cases, the children find the work they are given too hard for them, and they are naturally unable to concentrate on it.

Some children have been found to be deaf. This unrecognized barrier in communication has made them appear unresponsive to others and lacking in attention. Other children are so preoccupied with imaginary fears or worries that they have little energy left over to concentrate on school or play.

Obviously, it is not fair to expect parents to make diagnoses about their own children. If you recognize there is a serious problem, then you should discuss it first with your child's teacher, your health visitor, family doctor or paediatrician, rather than going directly to an agency that deals with nothing but hyper-

High energy does not necessarily mean there is anything wrong with your child.

activity and is not qualified to deal with other problems. Even when children are hyperactive, helping this problem in isolation is not always going to help their other problems.

No single cure?

Simon was a very premature baby. He needed special care in the first months of his life and had had several convulsions by the time he was one year old. The fits gradually disappeared, but it soon became clear that his ability to understand was not developing as quickly as in other children.

From about the age of two years he started to show a pattern of high activity that stayed with him for the next ten years. He could not concentrate on any outside activity for more than about ten seconds. He spent his days stamping around, briefly picking up toys in which he soon lost interest. Sometimes he spent hours rocking backwards and forwards with his hands in a bowl of water. When treatment began at the age of five, his speech was confined to grunts; but he still showed a boisterous affection for people he had never seen before.

His parents, teachers and therapists tried hard to help him to build up concentration, and he did make progress. But, even though his language improved (to a level of a six-year-old child when he was ten) and his concentration increased sufficiently for him to settle down with a teacher for ten- or fifteen-minute periods, he remained very behind in his learning and made no lasting friendships.

Simon was certainly hyperkinetic, but he had other problems as well. It would have been a mistake to focus all his education and treatment on that one problem. His intellectual retardation and his awkwardness with other children needed just as much help; and these problems did not greatly improve even when he grew out of the problem of hyperactivity. No single cure could be expected, whether from diet, drugs or psychotherapy. He needed a combination of therapy and education and, even then, his problems were by no means over.

Can hyperactivity be missed?

Hyperactivity can certainly go unrecognized if, for example, it is present with another problem that overshadows it.

Harold was referred to me for help, at the request of his school, when he was nine years old. The problem was his aggression and violence to others. He had pushed a boy through a window in a fight and stabbed another with scissors. Two previous schools had found him uncontrollable and had excluded him. Everyone who knew him regarded him as wildly overactive, unable to settle to anything, isolated from children of his own age, and quick to show physical anger when frustrated. This had been the pattern from his first years of life, but in addition he had certainly become increasingly moody. Much of his temper and insecurity seemed to be linked to a stormy life at home where arguments over his father's gambling often got out of control and escalated into physical violence.

Treatment began with a combination of family counselling and individual counselling for Harold, but it did not go well for him and he seemed to get little out of it. So, Harold was given a trial of a 'stimulant' medicine for his hyperactivity (see Chapter nine), with very positive and encouraging results. His concentration and self-control were greatly improved, enabling him to make much better use of psychological help from his therapists and teachers.

The various examples I have described by no means exhaust the ways overactivity and hyperactivity can present themselves. But they emphasize that every child is an individual who needs to be fully understood and not just diagnosed. They also illustrate some of the pitfalls in dealing with these problems.

Points to remember Here are some general points to be remembered if you are wondering whether your child is hyperactive:

- If your child has no evident disorder, then you do not need to imagine that he, or she, has a subtle variety of the condition lying hidden. Hyperactivity leads to real problems with personal adjustment. It can sometimes be difficult to know exactly what the problem is, but it is usually quite clear that a problem exists.
- Overactivity can be caused by many different kinds of stress. Discuss your child with friends and relatives who know him or her well: they may be able to point out these stresses and suggest ways to reduce them.
- Overactivity may be due to an abundance of energy and nothing else. If so, this is a sign of health, not disorder. Bright, vigorous children may well need to be occupied with a variety of activities – perhaps they need to play outside more often – but they are unlikely to need medical treatment.
- When your child's overactivity is associated with an inability to concentrate on anything for more than a few minutes or to apply any self-control in situations that demand reasonable behaviour and composure by the time of starting school, then you should consult your doctor.

- Before the age of three or four, the normal range of activity and attention is so wide that it is very difficult to detect anything but severe degrees of hyperactivity. If you are having problems in adjusting to your toddler's increased level of activity, advice can still be very useful. At this stage, there is no need to expect that the difficulty will go on to a persisting condition of hyperkinesis.

3

Physical causes of hyperactivity

Children differ greatly from one another, and this variation is not just the result of family environments. At one time, child psychologists (see page 89) believed that the way children were brought up determined the kind of people they became. While there is some truth in this, it falls far short of being the whole truth. Children living in similar environments are still very different from one another. Babies have very individual personalities even in the first days of life; and after that they influence their parents as well as being affected by them. This interaction is crucial for the development of a child's personality.

This chapter will describe some of the physical influences that can affect your child directly to make him more hyperactive. No one of them should be regarded as 'the cause' of your child's hyperactivity. Most of them need to be combined with other factors to have any influence. All of them operate together with the psychological factors I'll be describing in later chapters. Sometimes these physical causes are so strong that they produce major problems whatever the psychological environment is like, but this is not usually the case.

It is often fruitless to search back through time for one reason behind your child's problems. Often there is not one large cause but many small ones. Some people find this frustrating; they would prefer to pinpoint the problem to one definite cause. On the other

Bright, vigorous children may need to be occupied with a variety of activities.

hand, parents can sometimes feel guilty as they read through an account, like this, of possible causes and recognize things which may have affected their own child. It may be reassuring to you to know that there is probably no single culprit.

Some of the possible causes that I shall mention are still controversial. One of them – the nature of children's diets – has stirred up so much passion, both for and against, that it will need a chapter to itself (see page 55). Readers who would like to dig more deeply into the scientific evidence will find references for further reading at the end of the book.

TEMPERAMENT

A child's temperament is the first step in the formation of personality. It has several aspects, one of which is the general level of activity. This will naturally reveal itself in different ways at different ages.

A very active baby will probably respond directly to many different stimuli in the environment, and will move limbs about very vigorously when awake – though, quite possibly, sleep soundly. A toddler with a high activity level will climb, jump and run about most of the time. Many two- and three-year-olds are very active but there is still a big range of 'normal' activity at this age.

After three years, most children gradually settle down. A very active six-year-old may well be no more active than a normal three-year-old – but much more on the go than other children of the same age. A very active ten-year-old could apply himself to a number of activities and have many interests – or could have the unchannelled

The spectrum of activity levels. Only a small number of children are actually hyperactive.

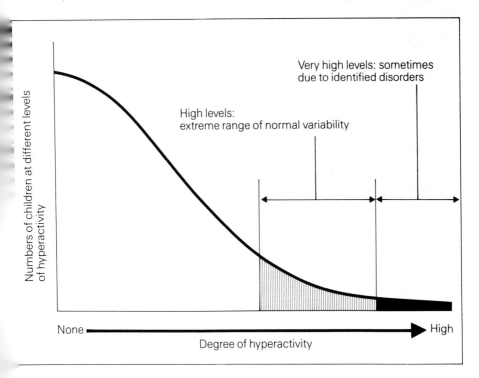

Temperamental dimensions

Underactive ◄———————— Activity ————————► Overactive

Regular ◄———————— Rhythmicity ————————► Irregular

Child alters greatly when   Child does not alter when
environment changes ◄——— Adaptability ——► environment changes

Approaches new   Withdraws from new
situations ◄—————— Approach-withdrawal ——————► situations

Responds only to   Responds to small
intense stimuli ◄————— Threshold ——————————► stimuli

Low energy of response ◄——— Intensity ———►High energy of response

Positive ◄———————— Mood ————————————► Negative

High ◄————————— Persistence ——————————————► Low

Low ◄——————————— Distractibility ——————————► High

An underactive and an overactive child have quite distinct temperaments that are reflected in activity levels and behaviour.

energy of a younger child. In other words, overactivity means different kinds of behaviour at different ages. Throughout development, children have a persistent style or way of doing things, although what they do may be quite unrelated.

Other differences   Although activity levels do vary greatly, this is not the only, or even the most important, way in which young children differ from each other. Another important difference is their attention span and persistence which, again, varies with age; also the extent to which children can adapt themselves to changes in their life, new things and people.

All these kinds of individual differences can lead to children being described as hyperactive, when they are just at the extreme end of the 'normal' spectrum. Other kinds of variability are less connected with hyperactivity; yet they can also determine the course of relationship patterns of children. Mood is one example;

a smiling, cheerful baby is much easier to live with than a crying, miserable baby. A fastidious, clean child can be easier for some people to cope with than a careless, untidy child.

Some American researchers have been very influential in establishing the ways in which we think of young children and how they differ from one another. Their variability has a number of different sources. Partly it is inherited, and partly it reflects the kind of environment in which children grow up.

One collection of these types of behaviour makes up 'the difficult child'. Intensity, misery, lack of adaptability, and poor attention are particularly marked. Being 'difficult' in this way is not exactly the same as being hyperactive. Behaviour difficulties in children are common and troublesome – for example, not sleeping; or throwing unusually severe temper tantrums. I shall say something in Chapters seven and eight about handling that kind of problem.

For now, I want to stress that these common behaviour problems do not in themselves mean that your child is hyperactive, nor that there is anything medically wrong. Hyperactivity can be one extreme of normal character. Like other aspects of character, it has multiple causes.

Effects of temperament on others

You may find it hard to understand your child's extremes of temperament. Usually you will find you can adjust to it and your child will respond to that adjustment. This is part of the development of a family. The process can go wrong. There can be a mismatch between child and parents.

Some parents find it easy to relate to a very active child, and even to a hyperactive one. They may well find his company fun and stimulating. Others find it much harder. This does not mean they are bad parents – perhaps they would be better than others at dealing with a withdrawn, timid, unassertive child.

There is no need to feel ashamed if you are at odds with your child in this way. It does not necessarily mean that there is anything wrong with you or with your child. It is still possible to have a good relationship with him or her, and even to value the good side of high activity. If that side includes determination and assertiveness, it may be very useful in later years.

BIOLOGICAL CAUSES

'Normal variation' is only one of the reasons for being restless and inattentive. Usually it is only the milder kind of hyperactivity that can be seen as this extreme of normal variability. The more serious kind of hyperactivity may have a biological cause.

Is hyperactivity inherited?

Physical and behavioural characteristics are passed down from parents to children by minute units of genetic material called genes. Humans have twenty-three pairs of chromosomes and each chromosome carries many genes. A child will receive approximately half his genes from his father and half from his mother. Brothers and sisters have, on average, half their genes in common (see diagram opposite).

Non-identical twins develop from two separate eggs (or ova) that are fertilized at the same time. Each twin has a different set of genes and the two children are not identical. Identical twins develop from a single fertilized ovum which splits into two foetuses. They therefore have exactly the same genes (see diagram opposite).

The more closely related a person is to a hyperactive child, the more likely that person is to show the same problem of behaviour. The activity level of identical twins is more alike than that of non-identical twins; full brothers are more alike than half-brothers.

This suggests that something is inherited that contributes to being hyperactive. This is not the whole story, for even identical twins can be different in their activity and attention. All the same, it does emphasize that children do not choose to have hyperactivity, it is not their fault, and it is not just a matter of faulty upbringing. More research about this is going on, and more still needs to be done.

Even if inheritance is important – and it may well be – this does not mean that it is the only cause of hyperactivity. On the contrary,

Top: A child receives approximately half his genes from his father and half from his mother, but the genes combine in different ways in each child to make them unique. *Bottom*: Identical and non-identical twins.

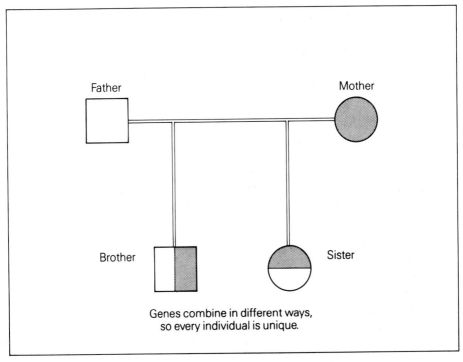

Genes combine in different ways,
so every individual is unique.

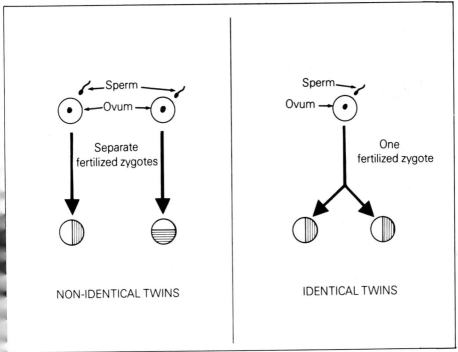

NON-IDENTICAL TWINS

IDENTICAL TWINS

it is quite clear that it is not all important. The great majority of brothers and sisters of hyperactive children are not themselves hyperactive. Furthermore, individual children do not necessarily develop hyperactivity even if they are vulnerable genetically. Whatever is inherited, it is not the hyperactivity itself. It might be a difference in chemistry of the brain, or a tendency to react to particular things in a certain way. Most people find ways to cope with whatever they have inherited and can even get some benefit from it.

Many parents who suffered from hyperactivity as children worry that they are passing it on to their children and on down the generations. However, even in the severe forms of hyperactivity, inheritance is only one factor amongst many others.

Does my child's sex matter?

The most obvious differences between children is their sex. Interestingly, there is a very big difference between girls and boys in terms of hyperactivity. Boys are three to four times more likely to suffer from the problem.

Partly this may be because girls are less likely to develop the other problems associated with hyperactivity – such as severe aggression – and therefore much less likely to be seen as having a problem that needs assessment and treatment. Girls are also expected to be quieter and to conform. But it has been suggested that some of the difference is because girls' brains develop in a more stable way than boys', and so they are less prone to any kind of delay in development.

Slow development

In some ways, hyperactivity could be described as a special kind of slow development.

Young children rush about more than older children, and though they often concentrate very intensely it is usually only for a short period. What is normal for a three-year-old at home would be a problem for an eight-year-old child with hyperactivity struggling to cope with friends, teachers and classroom learning. This means, of course, that judging whether a child is hyperactive has to be

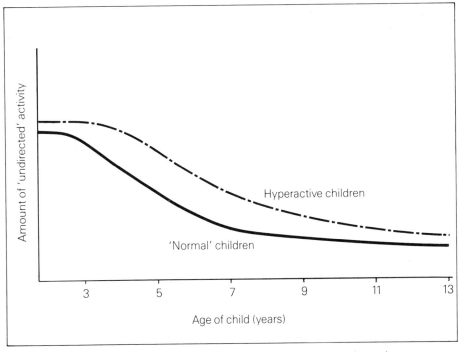

Hyperactive children have a greater amount of 'undirected' activity than 'normal children', but, as this diagram shows, activity levels in all children become more controlled as they grow older.

done as a comparison with the normal range of children of the same age. It also means that you can expect some lessening, even in very severe hyperactivity, as the child matures.

Children with hyperactivity are quite likely to show other kinds of slow development as well. Often, but not always, they are slow to begin talking, and remain behind with their understanding of language. This may make it more difficult for them to learn how to concentrate and organize themselves, and how to get on with other children. Sometimes, though again not always, children with hyperactivity are also slow learners, and this can cause problems in school (see Chapter four).

Pregnancy and birth

Toxaemia – more commonly known as pre-eclampsia – is a condition that affects women at an advanced state of pregnancy causing high blood pressure, swelling of the ankles and excretion of protein in the urine. Antenatal care ensures that it is detected early to protect your baby's development psychologically as well as physically. There is some evidence to suggest that pre-eclampsia may make it a little more likely that your child will be very active in the early years of life; but the effect is not strong. Most pregnancies complicated by pre-eclampsia still result in a normal child.

Occasionally some expectant mothers need to take male hormones during pregnancy, and this too can have consequences for the baby in the womb. The child can be more boisterous than others in early years – more like the stereotype of the active and exploring male! However, it has never been found that this is an important cause for the severe sort of hyperactivity that constitutes a problem for development.

Smoking and drinking alcohol during pregnancy are thought by many doctors to have a bad effect upon the child's later psychological development. Alcohol can cause the fetal alcohol syndrome, which includes hyperactivity in the child. The effect of tobacco smoke can cause baby animals in experiments to be born with hyperactive behaviour and a problem in learning. Neither tobacco nor alcohol are involved in most cases of hyperactivity in childhood, but sensible expectant mothers avoid them both.

Brain damage at birth

Complications during delivery can sometimes injure the baby's developing brain, or deprive it of oxygen for long enough to cause problems. One of the possible consequences is a behaviour disorder.

Nevertheless, most children who had a difficult birth grow up to be perfectly normal. Even if the brain itself is injured, this does not necessarily mean that there will be problems later. It seems to depend more upon the kind of psychological environment encountered during childhood. Some researchers say that if the child's psychological environment is all right then there is no longer any tendency for children with mild brain injury to develop hyperactivity later on. The real problems come when the injury is severe or when they grow up in some kind of adversity.

Just as the great majority of children injured at birth are not hyperactive, so most hyperactive children did not have problems at birth. One should definitely not assume that there must have been something subtly wrong. Like the other physical 'causes', early brain damage is usually one small factor among others in hyperactivity.

Brain injury after birth

For a few children, brain injury may come later in childhood – perhaps after being knocked down by a car. The damage has to be severe to cause behaviour problems later on – for example, if the injured child is unconscious for several days after the injury. A head injury that causes nothing more than a brief loss of consciousness is very unlikely to cause a lasting psychological problem.

Severe head injuries do not cause hyperactivity directly. Instead, they can lead to all kinds of psychological problems later. Misery, anxiety, frustration and aggression are all more probable results of such an injury than hyperactivity. Even when head injury has been the cause, hyperactivity can still be treated in the same way as when there is no obvious physical cause.

Recent research has applied brain imaging to studying whether there is anything wrong with the function of the brain in children with hyperactivity. At the time of writing, the results are suggesting that parts of the brain in hyperactive children are underfunctioning. Areas, especially the frontal lobes, that normally are involved in self-control and self-regulation are perhaps not working to their proper extent. This does not yet mean that brain damage is always the cause. There does not seem to be anything wrong with the anatomy of the brain, but only the way that it is being operated. An important aspect of this research is that it emphasizes the difference between a bright, active child and one who is hyperactive but whose brain is underactive.

Lead

Can lead be an important cause?   There has been a great deal of television and newspaper coverage of the effects of lead, and this has left much anxiety and confusion in its wake. The idea of invisible lead poisoning from the air we breathe, the food we eat and the water we drink is certainly alarming.

Too much anxiety over lead poisoning is unnecessary and unhelpful. The controversial level of exposure to lead is not a major factor in causing hyperactivity. It could well be a minor factor, and, at the time of writing, research is going on to try to establish whether it is or not. I shall describe some of the arguments for and against lead poisoning, to try to put the issues into perspective.

Severe lead poisoning   Everyone agrees that lead is a dangerous substance. If a child is seriously poisoned by lead, he or she can be very ill indeed. In the acute stage of the illness the child can suffer from fits and unconsciousness; even after recovery there may be signs of brain damage – for example, difficulty in concentrating, learning problems and hyperactive behaviour.

Happily, this kind of severe poisoning is rare. Something unusual needs to take place to bring about such a concentration; for example, stripping very old paint off a house. Up until the 1950s, most house paints contained lead. Stripping old paint can result in a massive amount of lead in the dust that is then breathed in or eaten in contaminated food. It makes sense to check whether paint could be dangerous before stripping it.

Where does lead come from?   Even in an ordinary environment, we cannot escape some contact with lead. Lead pipes will contaminate the water flowing through them. Areas with soft water are particularly prone to higher lead levels, because lead from pipes dissolves more readily in soft water. Some food contains lead, especially tinned food. Dust, perhaps from flaking old paint or industrial contamination, may contain lead.

Some industrial processes such as smelting, or recycling car batteries, can free lead into the environment. Lead compounds are added to petrol to prevent 'knocking' and will therefore discharge lead into the air through exhaust fumes. Although the quantity of lead in petrol is small it is easily absorbed by the body, because of the chemical form it is in.

As lead comes from a variety of sources, the amount of lead in a person's body will also vary. The concern is not that this variation causes severe symptoms of poisoning, but that it might have more subtle effects. Nobody really knows how little is safe.

Safe levels?   Until about five years ago, experts generally thought that the safe level was below 40 mg of lead per 100 ml of blood. Since then, a great deal of research has been carried out. It has revealed that, even below this level, some children with higher quantities of lead in their blood or teeth are also more likely to have difficulty in concentrating and doing psychological tests than other children. It is not a close relationship. Most hyperactive children do not have high lead levels. Nevertheless, careful studies have agreed that some form of link can be found.

That by itself does not mean that the lead has caused the problem. It could well be the other way round: the more reckless and impulsive a child is, the more likely he is to breathe in or eat contaminated dust. Or it could be that children who are living in the kind of poor social conditions that bring them in close contact with lead become more hyperactive because of other, independent, aspects of a deprived upbringing. Research has not yet answered the question: which comes first, the behaviour problem or the lead? This leaves some uncertainty about how far one should go to reduce children's exposure to lead.

Reducing lead exposure

There are some drugs available that actually remove lead from the body; for example, penicillamine. But all the drugs that are known to be effective have quite serious side-effects. A few people taking the drugs have suffered damage to the kidneys and other organs in the body.

For this reason, the drugs are only prescribed to children who have such high levels of lead in their bodies that they are definitely and unequivocally at risk. You can buy some much safer compounds over-the-counter that are supposed to counteract lead

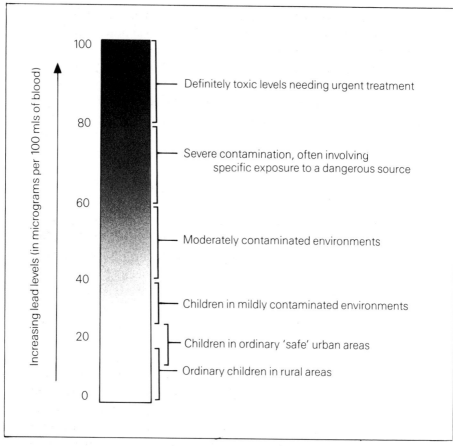

The spectrum of lead exposure.

toxicity. They often include pectin, zinc and aminoacids. It is very doubtful, however, whether these safer substances are effective in counteracting lead exposure.

I do not recommend parents to try to treat lead exposure in this way. Some parents certainly do, often on the basis of relatively unreliable estimates of the amount of lead in the air. This is unwise for two reasons. Firstly, if the level of lead in the body is not too high, then trying to treat it is a waste of money and time and can also be a distraction from more important problems that need tackling. Secondly, if the level of lead is dangerously high it is too serious a matter for half-measures. It should only be treated under medical supervision.

Prevention is better than cure, and in this instance it is much safer. One step towards prevention is the removal of lead additives from petrol, and many countries, including Britain, North America and Australia, are taking steps to do this. Eliminating lead from paint is another step, but there is still a good deal of lead-contaminated paint on older buildings. Replacing lead waterpipes in soft-water areas would be another step. If you have lead waterpipes, it may be helpful simply to run the water for a few seconds before drinking it or using it for cooking.

What should you do about lead poisoning?

- Do not assume that hyperactivity is caused by lead because it usually isn't. Even the small, subtle and controversial degrees of exposure to lead could only account for a small proportion of cases.
- Avoid commercial and non-medical enterprises that claim to diagnose and treat lead poisoning.
- Be alert to the possibility that your home or your child's school may be close to some sort of lead pollution.
- If you are suspicious about environmental influences – for example if you live in a housing area that is predominantly pre-1950 and still has much old paint, or there is a car battery plant close by – then environmental health departments can and do sample dust and paint and so on, to confirm or dispel your doubts. If there is real contamination by lead, your children may need to be tested and public health measures taken to reduce the exposure.
- Finally, even if lead exposure does need to be reduced, do not suppose that this means your child has necessarily been contaminated or that lead is the only cause of a problem. The contribution of lead to hyperactivity and other behaviour problems is small, and just one factor among very many others.

OTHER PHYSICAL ILLNESSES

When children feel ill, they tend to be irritable. They may well lose concentration and behave badly. This can happen with any illness. Usually it is obvious because the illness comes first, but sometimes the illness is hidden. If your previously normal child starts to become hyperactive, then something is wrong. He may be reacting to a stress but whatever the cause, you should consult your doctor about the possibility of a physical illness.

Some physical conditions are chronic and begin early in childhood. The most relevant to hyperactivity are deafness and visual handicap. Severe deafness will usually be obvious, but minor degrees can go unrecognized for a long time. Recurrent ear infections can lead to a situation in which a child is partially deaf for weeks at a time but then returns to normal. If routine medical examinations fall during the normal intervals, the doctor could fail to pick up the problem. Intermittent deafness can be particularly unsettling for a child, causing a change in behaviour and possibly an increase in the level of activity.

You should consult a doctor if:

- Your child's language development is slower than that of other children;
- You notice that he is closely watching your lips when you speak and relies a great deal on gesture;
- He does not recognize meaningful household sounds, such as the noise of food being prepared before a meal;
- You notice that things are much worse after a cold.

Recurrent headaches and allergic reactions are further, but less common, examples of physical conditions that can disrupt school and family life (see Chapter six). There is no scientific evidence to support theories that explain all cases of hyperactivity in terms of altered body chemistry.

In summary, brain damage can cause hyperactivity – but most children with hyperactivity do not have damaged brains. The majority of affected children, especially those with milder problems, show an extreme of normal temperament, or a kind of slow development, or both. Temperament and slow development are both partly inherited, but only partly: biological causes are seldom the sole cause, and interact with psychological factors in causing hyperactivity.

4

Hyperactive children at school

By the time children start school, they have already had to adjust a number of times to different environments and events. School brings a new set of stresses and opportunities.

Some children, who have already been identified as hyperactive, do very well once their school careers begin. These are often the children who were very active rather than truly hyperactive in their earlier childhood. They may well have been bright, boisterous and energetic; but they are also likely to have been able to organize themselves, to recognize when relative quietness is necessary, and to make good contact with other children. For children like this, the variety of activities available in a class and the stimulus of social life with other children can come as very welcome outlets. Their energy finds constructive channels.

School solves the problem

Michael was referred to a psychiatric clinic when he was nearly four years old. He had learned to walk at an early age, and from that time he seemed to be continually in top gear: whatever he did, he did it with great intensity. When a television programme interested him, he would watch it for hours. At night he needed substantially less sleep than his parents, and lay awake until one or two in the morning, singing loudly, playing and occupying himself.

Some overactive children do very well once their school careers begin, and find the variety of activities and the stimulus of other children very welcome outlets for their excess energy.

His escapades had already become a minor local legend: he discovered, for instance, that he could lock his parents out of the house and laugh at their efforts to get in. Just before he was referred to the clinic, he had taken his father's car keys, climbed out of the window of their ground-floor flat, started the car engine and taken off the brake. Happily, the slope of the road was slight and the car simply struck the next car parked in the street.

Evaluation at the clinic found nothing wrong with his development. On the contrary, he was well ahead of his years in his language and his ability to solve puzzles. An early entry into school was arranged, and at once he enjoyed himself enormously and settled down considerably at home. A full IQ assessment, carried out later, showed him to be in the 'very superior' range.

Michael showed how school can add a new and challenging experience to the life of a hyperactive child. In addition, Michael's intelligence helped him to understand and cope with the demands of the different worlds in which he lived.

Other children, whether or not they have encountered problems in their family life, find the new demands of the school world to be all too much. The exact nature of the difficulty differs from child to child.

Some find the new environment bewildering and full of distractions. They become disorganized in it and rush from point to point or to whatever fleeting change has most recently caught their attention. But they need not necessarily be distressed by this. Indeed, they may well be over excited and apparently cheerful, at least to start with. The strain is felt by other people. Teachers may find them exhausting or disruptive. Other children are quick to turn away from another child who is acting in a silly way, or interfering with what they want to do. The stage is set for a drama of increasing isolation and resentment.

Many hyperactive children find that the hardest thing to cope with at school is the lack of their usual supports; in most cases, their parents. While those who are firmly attached to either or both parents have a sound base from which they can explore the new world, it is very difficult for those children who have already encountered rejection. They are perhaps the most likely to be distressed and angry as well as difficult; they may forbid their mother to leave and throw rages.

Both these patterns – becoming disorganized in a new environment and becoming stressed by separation – are shown to a mild extent by many children. Both can be simply a part of adjusting to a new environment; and they will disappear as school becomes more familiar. You should not worry unless your child's reaction to school is intense and persistent. Both can often be helped by a gradual introduction to this new experience.

Sometimes a child's hyperactivity makes difficulty in settling down in school, but it is not recognized as such. Teachers may think that the child is being deliberately naughty, or that an emotional upset is responsible. This is particularly likely to happen in countries, such as England, where hyperactivity is not recognized as an educational problem. If your child is having serious problems, and they do not seem to be getting better with the commonsense approaches of increasing security and being firm but warm in discipline, then it can be very helpful to have an expert's opinion. Educational psychologists can be brought in by the schools and they will often be in a very good position to detect that a problem in concentrating and self-organizing is at the heart of the apparently bad behaviour.

Would playgroup help?

Nursery classes and playgroups help children to adjust to other children, and a parent's presence is often useful. Unfortunately, these preschool experiences are often hardest to acquire when they are needed most.

Very difficult children are often asked to leave such classes, precisely because they make life unpleasant for the others or because 'they are not ready for it'. They may well be less ready for it than other children – but they will not suddenly become ready for the increased expectations of infant school when the time comes. Some schools make it easy for children to stay in a less mature setting if they need to, but not all schools can be as flexible about this.

If you are having problems with your child, it may work best to build up school attendance fairly gradually and for you to stay present and involved in the classroom. This is not always possible, of course; but if it is possible, don't let shyness or diffidence deter you. Most teachers nowadays will welcome it – and will also say clearly if you ought to leave your child alone for a spell.

As schooling proceeds, many more steps will have to be taken towards academic learning, self-control and the making of friendships. If these stages progress well, it need not matter that some hyperactivity continues. If problems arise, it is often because the hyperkinesis was severe.

ATTENTION PROBLEMS

Paying attention   In order to learn, your child has to concentrate. Teachers expect and encourage a gradually lengthening attention span, so that children learn to take in more information at each stage. Eventually, and certainly by secondary school, whole periods need to be devoted to a single subject.

The attention problem that is a central part of the hyperkinetic syndrome therefore acts as a real brake on progress. The longer it persists, the farther behind an affected child will drop.

What can be done about an attention problem?   It is easiest to start by listing remedies that are *not* usually helpful. Exasperated scolding – for example, 'why can't you try harder?' or 'for heaven's sake, concentrate' – is not useful. Hyperactive children do not intend to be the way they are, cannot understand the reasons for acting the way they do, and cannot change simply at a word of command. Furthermore, it does not usually make much difference if you try to insulate them from outside noise and distraction. Even if they are sitting away from other children, they can still be distracted by minor disturbances around them.

A much better strategy is simply to accept that there is a problem, and for teachers to pitch the teaching appropriately. This means, for example, that when your child has to learn something new in class, it is better to break it up into small steps so that each one can be mastered in a fairly short space of time. This also allows your child time for letting off steam between each step. Even if each time space is as short as a few seconds, the end result is likely to be better than the outcome of lengthy and continuous lessons.

Another part of the learning strategy is to emphasize what is important. Normally, children progress from letting their attention be taken by whatever is brightest, loudest, or most attractively coloured towards recognizing and focussing on the main logical aspects of a problem. Children with attention problems find this very difficult, and may simply need to have things presented to them in a more structured way. You can achieve this by putting emphasis on what is important for them to notice.

Remedial teaching

A second strategy is to concentrate directly on the attention abilities that are lagging behind. This may entail a treatment programme of the kind described in Chapter nine. Less formally, it may simply mean encouraging gradual steps in the direction of better concentration.

There are in fact several abilities to encourage.

- One of them is the willingness to persist for set periods of time at a task; it may help to give systematic rewards for longer periods spent on activities. Chapter seven describes a reward scheme for parents to use; teachers sometimes follow similar tactics.
- Another skill to encourage is that of pausing and reflecting when asked a question or presented with a problem. Fast, impulsive answers are often wrong, and you should encourage your child to slow down and think reflectively before answering.
- Children gradually learn to build up the art of dividing attention; that is, of noticing several things at the same time and picking out the most crucial. Some remedial teachers may encourage your child to do this by teaching him to talk to himself about what he is doing and so notice what he has to do; for example to repeat phrases such as 'stop and think' or 'what kind of problem is this?' to himself.

There is no contradiction between these two ways of helping to repair a handicap – by recognizing the problem and trying to skirt round it – and by remedial teaching. The balance is part of the education of every handicapped child. In this particular instance, the most difficult task can be to recognize that a handicap is present. Not being able to pay attention is a subtle problem, and often masquerades as idleness and naughtiness.

Poor concentration is a handicap even when children are left to their own devices. Much of education consists of what pupils find out for themselves, and how they actively make sense of their world. Their curiosity is more important in the long run than their willingness to listen to what adults tell them. Superficially, children with hyperkinesis may seem to be exploring a great deal. But there is a fundamental difference between their inefficient exploring and the constructive curiosity of bright, alert children. The exploration of the hyperkinetic child is brief, scattered and repetitive. It does not lead on to ideas and the testing of ideas, but simply to another round of exploration. It does not sustain interest; rather, a teacher has to provide outside interest in the forms of novelty, change and humour.

Lacking the ability to concentrate, therefore, sets a challenge for teachers in many ways. First, they need to recognize it and then have to set their teaching at the child's individual level of development.

Language, IQ and learning problems

Hyperkinesis is found in children of all intellectual levels. It is neither a sign of giftedness nor of retardation. But it tends to be associated with a low level of achievement in a number of activities, including IQ tests. There are probably several reasons for this. A child who is slow to learn, for whatever reason, will also be slower to learn the skills of concentration and self control. A child with poorly developed concentration will be held back from other kinds of learning.

A similar relationship probably occurs in language development. Poor concentration can delay language. Yet, some children can be taught to use inner language to control their attention, and this is the basis of one method of therapy (see page 81). Whatever the cause of the language delay, it can contribute to hyperactivity.

In summary, attention deficit is just one of the many risk factors that can lead to problems in learning. A child with a learning problem needs to be professionally assessed and may need several different kinds of help. You should not assume that hyperkinesis is the only problem, and also not imagine that it is an easy answer for all educational failures.

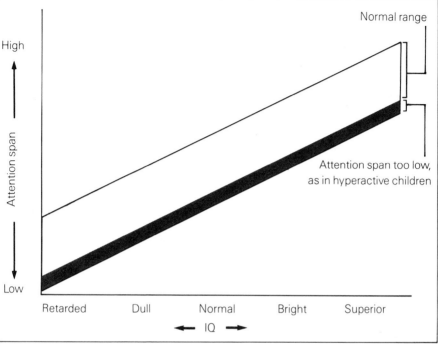

High

Attention span

Low

Normal range

Attention span too low,
as in hyperactive children

Retarded   Dull   Normal   Bright   Superior

← IQ →

Children with hyperactivity have a low attention span and find it difficult to concentrate.
They may fall behind at school as a result.

Antisocial behaviour in the classroom

Children who fall behind in their education tend to develop other
problems as well. For example, nearly half of the children who are
severely behind with their reading also behave in an antisocial way,
which may lead them into truancy, aggression and stealing. They
become used to failure; they become disaffected, vulnerable and
despair of themselves.

Preventing this needs positive efforts and teamwork from both
teachers and parents. If communications between school and home
deteriorate, then the child suffers. One example of this need for
communication is in the teacher's attempt to keep discipline. A
child who is wildly out of control can sometimes be helped by a
'good conduct report system'. Teachers explicitly notice and write

down the good things that he has done – and there are always some! This form of communication is just as important for the children as for the parents. It pinpoints things for parents to encourage and reward.

'Good conduct report system' in practice

A good example of this approach was adopted for Harold, whose difficulties were described in Chapter two (see page 14). He took a diary to school with him every day and divided each page into the number of lessons in the day. At each lesson his teacher was responsible for checking three things: whether he arrived on time, whether he had finished an assignment (which the teacher made specially short for him), and whether he had got to the end of the lesson without punching or kicking anybody else. At home in the evening, he won extra television viewing time depending on how many ticks he had achieved that day.

There were two signs that this system was useful for Harold, in spite of its crudeness. Firstly, he won gradually more ticks, and therefore more rewards, each week. Secondly, he became happier and more hopeful about school with the shift away from repetitive punishment. His better motivation made it possible for him to sit down with a teacher and make his hesitant, inaccurate reading more fluent.

How to discipline a hyperactive child?

A breakdown in communication between parents and teachers may often result when there is a clash of ideas about discipline. You need to talk them through with mutual respect. This is common sense for anyone, not just those with hyperkinesis. Hyperkinesis is important in this context because it is one of the routes through which some children arrive at their problem of behaviour. As with disorders of learning (see page 40), hyperactivity is just one possible cause among many. In some countries, for example North America and Australia, a large proportion of the children who behave badly or aggressively in their class are regarded as hyperactive and treated accordingly. The danger is that teachers can then lose sight of the other possible causes. In other countries,

A good conduct report diary

Period	Monday September 14th		
	In right place at beginning of lesson	Assignment finished	Did not punch or kick anyone
9.15	✓ YES	✓ YES	✓ YES
10.30 (after break)	✓ YES		
11.30		✓ YES	
2.00	✓ YES		✓ VERY GOOD
3.00	✓ YES	A better day, Harold	

The 'good conduct report system' adopted by Harold's teacher.

teachers fail to recognize how useful it can be to concentrate on teaching children to control their own impulsiveness.

Making friends

Severely hyperkinetic children often do not fit into the company of other children. They are often very unpopular, and do not understand how to change themselves for the better.

The normal process of making friends is subtle and reciprocal. A child joining a group has to learn the group rules and the games they play; only after this learning process can he start to influence the other members of the group. Similarly, two schoolchildren starting to play together begin by sharing activities, taking turns, revealing things about themselves and finding out about one another. A child who is impatient, who does not conform and has few feelings for others is likely to be excluded and isolated. Instead, he leaps in without restraint and tries to mould others, failing to follow all the complexities of a group.

Adults need to show hyperkinetic children how to control themselves, and how to take turns; and some do indeed learn from this. You may find it very painful to see your child being provoked by others, or left out of things. The best way you can help is probably to encourage him not to give up but to go on playing with others, even in the face of rebuffs, and to learn from their reactions. Quiet and friendly explanations of how other children feel are another way you can encourage social learning.

What kind of school should you choose?

There is no single answer to the question of how to educate hyperkinetic children. The severely hyperkinetic are likely to have several problems, and so, from their point of view, the school needs to be flexible and to treat children in terms of their individual needs. Both a large and a small school can provide this, as can a special or mainstream school. Often atmosphere and leadership are more important than anything else.

Several of the teaching techniques have been mentioned above, but none of them is crucial in itself to the choice of school. Sometimes, parents are recommended a special school so that their child can have the benefit of one approach – such as behaviour modification (see page 97) or intensive remedial teaching (for example, one-to-one teaching). The decision is based much more on what is available locally than on any theoretical knowledge about what schooling is best.

An educational psychologist (see page 89) is usually the person in the best position to match your child's needs to a particular school. It is still a matter for debate whether hyperactive children should be given special teaching in separate schools or whether 'normal' schools should deploy extra resources to teach them. Many parts of Britain are changing from the first approach to the second. In North America the approach varies a great deal. But there can be no ideal general decision. I often recommend that children with severe hyperactivity are helped best by having an extra adult – perhaps a teacher's aide – spending part of the day in the classroom to help the child recognize what they need to do, to slow themselves down, and to be patient with other children. It may well be possible for that aide to use simple behaviour therapy measures (see page 97).

The choice for parents is all the harder in Britain because the idea of childhood hyperkinesis is not accepted in many educational circles. There are, at the time of writing, no specialist units or schools just for hyperactive children. Indeed, the severe hyperkinesis to which I am referring is quite uncommon. As a result, I see a number of children who are, in effect, 'odd man out' in their own schools.

The kind of school that is chosen will therefore depend upon which type of problem is foremost in the particular case. For some, the most handicapping aspect is the failure to concentrate and learn. Schools for slow learners are the logical place for these children. For others, schooling is interrupted by their disruptive behaviour. They may be recommended to a school for 'maladjusted' pupils. Children with movement disorders and delayed language development may well achieve most in classes for the physically handicapped.

One of the main themes of this book is to point out that complications which accompany the problem are often more serious than the original hyperactivity. It is obviously sound to concentrate on the major difficulties. But I believe that parents' groups should now campaign for more debate, research and planning about the educational needs of the severely hyperkinetic.

5

The influences of family relationships

Family relationships do not completely explain children's problems, but they are powerful influences upon them. Parents need to recognize both sides of this, to avoid extremes of self blame on the one hand and irresponsibility on the other.

It is common for the parents of a hyperactive child to blame themselves – and also for them to find themselves blamed by others. This can be unfair and unnecessary, and if the ensuing guilt makes them less able to be effective parents, it can harm their children. Equally, some parents slide into the opposite position of denying their own role in their children's development, thereby absolving themselves of responsibility.

There are, of course, as many kinds of family relationships as there are families. The purpose of this chapter is to describe some of the common patterns that can make life harder for hyperactive children.

Other members of the family can be important in several ways:

- They can determine whether or not a child is recognized as hyperactive.
- They can react to hyperactivity in a way that accentuates other problems.
- They can contribute to the initial development of hyperactivity.

RECOGNIZING HYPERACTIVITY

Parents are often the first to recognize and label their child as hyperactive. This can be very helpful for the child's development, and parents will sometimes have to fight to communicate to others their understanding of their child's condition. There can, however, also be problems if parents have to do the work of identification themselves. Occasionally this is done without sufficient knowledge and understanding of the problem. A normal child can sometimes be incorrectly identified as hyperactive, and this can be a serious matter if it alters the way that he or she is subsequently treated. Several factors can contribute to the misunderstanding of the word hyperactive, highlighted in Chapter one. If a high level of activity by itself is made into a problem – as some accounts in the media would suggest – then a vast number of parents will be led into diagnosing their children. This will be all the more probable for parents who do not have a wide experience of children, who are isolated from other people or who come from a culture with different standards of expectation of how children should behave.

Another set of causes come into play when parents are them-selves under stress. If, for instance, a parent becomes very depressed and despondent about something, then it is all too easy to let this mood affect everything else. Abnormal childish high spirits can then become intolerable, and minor failings can become magnified into evidence of 'a problem'. Sometimes one child in a family becomes a scapegoat and every kind of family tension is blamed upon him. 'Hyperactivity' can then be a term of abuse and an accusation of abnormality.

Dewi is an only child of Indian parents who were forced to flee as political refugees from a Middle Eastern country. They lost everything, including their professional careers, and settled in London in poverty. His father found menial work and his mother remained at home with no adult contacts at all except her husband who returned home in the evening. Her aspirations for her son turned sour when he was still wetting the bed at the age of six, and when at much the same age he was resisting instructions to go to bed and running naughtily out of the room. Neither of these 'problems' is in fact abnormal, or even

Family relationships can make a great impact upon the way hyperactive children develop.

unusual, in British boys of that age; but to his mother they seemed like evidence of a 'disease' of his brain. She took reassurance from her doctor to mean that nothing could be done. She took herself and her child as an emergency to a psychiatric hospital, and said she would kill herself if he was not admitted for treatment of his brain. Indeed, even after treatment for herself, and even after Dewi's bed-wetting had stopped, she can still not accept that he is a resilient and 'normal' boy. Nevertheless, she is now less isolated and correspondingly less preoccupied with his condition.

The remedy is to be able to talk over worries about your child with other people you can trust. Others who know your child are probably ideal; particularly teachers, or playgroup leaders. Nevertheless, your child can be so different in other settings that you may hear descriptions of what sounds like another child entirely.

It can also be very useful to compare notes directly with other parents, and to ask your health visitor's advice (or that of paediatrician or community nurse in the United States). Pay no attention to the glamorized picture of family life that advertisers and attendant journalists often try to convey! They are often completely unrealistic!

REACTING TO HYPERACTIVITY

The vicious cycle of conflict   When children are very restless, they obviously tend to come into conflict with adult authority. Discipline can then be much more of a problem. It is easy to preach calmness, good tempered firmness and consistency as recipes for sensible handling. Indeed, the advice so far as it goes is good. Practising these virtues, however, may well require more patience and self confidence than you can always muster. When they fail badly, the stage is set for vicious cycles of increasing hostility.

The first steps occur when a parent reacts to a child's restlessness with angry punishment. The child reacts to that response with more anger and confrontation. This is also a kind of punishment for the parent, and the dispute escalates. Later in this cycle, child and parent each get into a habit of controlling the other through punishment and threat (see diagram overleaf). Both are resentful, and the child may be frightened too, yet unable to stop. Good, loving or even friendly contacts between the two become less frequent, and this in itself poisons the relationship further. The outcome can then create a bitter and tense family atmosphere. Children often start to be aggressive or antisocial outside their homes and consequently get into trouble with the law. Sometimes the extreme is reached and a child is physically battered.

Nobody wants to go down this road – but all too many do. Of course, it is not inevitable. Most families manage to avoid it, and prevention is a good deal easier than cure. Nor is it necessarily the result of hyperactivity, for many other things can trigger off this reaction.

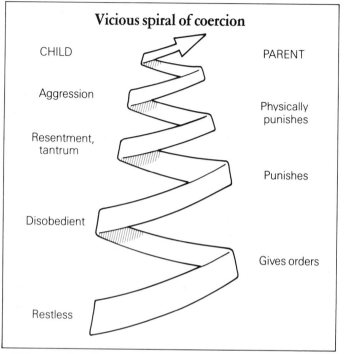

Vicious spiral of coercion

CHILD

PARENT

Aggression

Physically
punishes

Resentment,
tantrum

Punishes

Disobedient

Gives orders

Restless

To prevent this cycle of conflict, recognize the problem, defuse tense situations and bring back the positive, warm contact necessary to maintain control.

The way to avoid it is:

- Firstly, to recognize the problem;
- Secondly, to find ways of defusing tense situations and bringing back the positive and warm contacts that act as the necessar background against which control can be maintained;
- Thirdly, to accept outside help when it is needed.

Chapters seven and eight take these points further.

Tyranny and 'I have to'

A quite different cycle can develop if conflict is reduced at the price of abandoning adult control. Parents may allow themselves to be tyrannized by their child, and find themselves saying things like: 'I have to have her in bed with us, or she would scream and scream'; or 'I have to dress him in his school clothes while someone else amuses him, or he would never get ready'. These are obviously not damaging acts in themselves, but they do suggest that parental authority is being abandoned.

If this is the case, you are not doing your child a favour. It gives most children no pleasure to be in charge of everything that happens. On the contrary, they often feel frightened, or perhaps are driven to challenge the limits of authority in ever more outrageous ways. It can then come as a real relief to be 'treated as a child' again, and to have clear and consistent rules affirmed.

One of the ways into this kind of pattern stems from the fact that being indulgent obviously works. If, for instance, a very active and intense six-year-old has smashed up his brother's toys then it certainly keeps the peace if the brother is forbidden to object and the parents hold themselves back from any reaction. In the short term, there is no confrontation, no tantrum, and life is easier.

On the other hand, in the long term this has probably made things worse. The six-year-old is more likely to do it again – in a sense, he has been allowed and encouraged to. At a later stage the same parents might attempt to buy off the anger of other children, and their families, to whom their son has been aggressive; or allow him to keep things he has stolen from shops and pay the shopkeeper themselves.

Many children with severe hyperactivity find it difficult to see the links between their actions and the consequences of what they do. If they are protected, through indulgence, from the normal results of their actions, they are also deprived of an essential piece of learning.

Arguments and inconsistency between parents

One of the commonest sources of argument between parents is how to bring up their children. Since there is no one right way and since husband and wife bring different experiences and ideas to the task, the only surprise is perhaps that most people sort things out so well. Nevertheless, rifts and disagreements are often deepened when the task is made harder by a 'difficult' temperament in their child. This need not be a serious matter. Disagreements can usually be talked over and resolved in discussion. They become serious when ordinary good channels of communication are blocked.

When parents can find no resolution, this can easily make life harder for the children. Inconsistency is confusing for everyone, but especially for children with hyperactivity who have to struggle harder than most to work out the subtle, complicated rules that govern social life. Open conflict and bitterness between parents are worse than confusing, for they undermine the child's main basis of security.

Unresolved disagreements tend to get worse. The actions of one parent tend to force the other into a more extreme version of their original position. For example, a mother may think that her husband's strictness is too harsh for their son, so she tries to make up for it by providing more comfort and indulgence. Her husband then sees this as weak pampering and redoubles his own efforts to be firm and authoritarian. Each is forcing the other away from the middle ground. Conflict then becomes stronger; or else one parent – typically, but not necessarily, the father – opts out completely, relinquishes his role, and thereby conveys a sense of rejection to his child; once again making matters worse.

It is pointless to blame your child for this kind of situation. It may well have been your child's actions that triggered it off in the first place but it would be quite outside his or her ability to change the whole pattern of relationships once it has developed. It is up to the adults to make the first move and to begin the painful processes of compromise, bargaining and good will. Sometimes good will is not enough, and outside help is needed.

The important point is that help sometimes needs to be concentrated on the whole pattern of family relationships, not solely upon the child. Chapters seven and eight discuss some of the ways in which changes can be made.

Can bad relationships cause hyperactivity?

The patterns I have just described started with a child who was chaotic and restless. The implication was that the root cause lay in the child's own development, but as I have pointed out this is not always true. There is a continuing scientific controversy about the relative importance of nature and nurture; that is, the effects of inheritance and the effects of upbringing. Probably both operate, and tend to reinforce each other.

Children have to learn how to organize their attention, and an important part of this learning takes place in the first five years of life in association with the adults who are looking after them. To begin with, babies explore the world mainly by looking. They tend to follow the line of their mother's gaze, and look where she looks. Correspondingly, mothers learn about the objects that interest their baby and can point them out. In theory, therefore, anything that disrupts this mutual sensitivity could delay the process by which the child learns how to organize his or her attention.

Nobody knows for certain whether this possibility actually works in practice, but there are some clues that it may. For example, children who have grown up in an orphanage are more likely to be overactive and to concentrate poorly than other children. They have not been physically neglected, but they have not had the constancy of relationship that a mother can provide. Obviously, this example only applies to a small minority of children with hyperactivity, but it raises the real possibility that a deprived family upbringing will tend to create restless and immature children. If family life is very chaotic, and children's activities are always being interrupted, then they may just not have the chance to learn how to be persistent.

Hyperactivity – or a deprived home?

Matilda was taken into the care of the local authority when she was three years old. She had been neglected as a baby, to the point of needing hospital treatment for malnutrition and bruising. As a result a judge had ordered that she be separated from her parents. A foster family could not manage her, so she was then placed in a voluntary children's home with eleven other children.

The home was a good one, friendly and pleasant, but her development continued to fall behind that of the other children. When I saw her, at the age of eight, her speech was very immature and she often became frustrated and screamed. An attempt was made to increase her language ability and vocabulary, by encouraging her to talk more with the staff at the home.

Unfortunately, this was very difficult to organize. The need to occupy and stimulate all the children in the group meant that lengthy and leisurely conversations with an adult were hard to get, and even then were interrupted by the more articulate children.

Society places burdens upon those running children's homes which often defeat the purpose of the truly home-like environment they are trying to create. Also society often fails to relieve the burdens of parents who become overwhelmed.

Too strict a punishment

Another contribution to hyperactivity that I have occasionally seen comes from an unwise use of restraint, and is best described by this example.

Jeffrey's parents tried to manage his three-year-old unruliness with strictness, and had found that they could punish him effectively by making him sit quietly in a corner of the room for a period of fifteen minutes. Unfortunately, but not surprisingly, this meant that Jeffrey emerged at the end of the enforced period with an explosion of pent-up energy that rapidly got him into trouble again.

By the time I saw Jeffrey at the age of six, he was only 'good' when he was being punished – but the punishment was responsible for his naughtiness. His parents had to learn a different kind of restraint. They changed their style by letting Jeffrey have a spell of intense, boisterous play as a reward for quieter play. Their own reward – after a few stormy weeks – was a happier and more manageable son.

In summary, family relationships can make a great impact upon the way that hyperactive children develop. But, so far as we know, they are only occasionally the prime cause of hyperactivity. Nevertheless, the main difficulties in coping with a hyperactive child can be accentuated by the other unrelated difficulties in family life. The first step towards avoiding the pitfalls described in this chapter is to recognize their possibility. The kind of help that the family can give is described in more detail in Chapter seven.

6

Using and abusing diets

Any mention of hyperactivity will automatically lead many people to think of special diets as effective treatments. Most of the books and articles intended for parents these days stress that the main cause of the problem is an intolerance to certain foods, and that the main treatment is to avoid them. Most support groups for parents of hyperactive children promote exclusion diets as a central treatment. Anyone on this type of diet must entirely exclude certain foods (for example, eggs, wheat and cow's milk) that research has shown cause discomfort and illness to a number of people. After an exclusion period, the individual foods are slowly reintroduced in a specific order to try to pinpoint the culprit.

My own experience has led me to a mixed conclusion. Some hyperactive children are helped very much by excluding the particular foods – different for each child – to which they have become intolerant. It is worth keeping a diary to see if you can relate your child's behaviour to the eating of particular foods. Unfortunately, however, it is only a minority of hyperactive children who respond well to the diets. So, it is important not to press on with ever more and more strict diets if a child is not doing well. Foods are an important cause for a few children, but for most hyperactive children they do not contribute. In this chapter, I shall go into the evidence for and against diets in a little more detail than for other possible causes so that you can judge for yourselves.

The Feingold diet

The best known treatment is the Feingold diet, named after the doctor who devised it. It requires that one should completely avoid eating foods that contain artificial colours, some preservatives, and salicylates (see below). In practice this means eliminating a wide variety of manufactured, frozen and processed foods.

Salicylates are naturally occurring chemicals (rather similar to aspirin) that are found in many fruits; for example, apples, bananas, blueberries, grapes, plums, prunes, rhubarb and strawberries. Food labels should tell you just which preservatives have been added, so it is often a matter of trial and error to find out which foods need avoiding.

Manufacturers also add many artificial colourings to foods; they must all be eliminated in the Feingold diet (at least to begin with). Erythrosine, a red dye, and tartrazine, an orange dye, have both been particularly under scrutiny for other reasons. Erythrosine causes the release of chemical substances from the nerve cells of animals that can cause changes in behaviour; tartrazine, used in fruit squashes and many other foods, is known to cause allergic reactions. Nevertheless, there is no strong reason to think that dyes other than erythrosine and tartrazine are any safer.

I believe nobody actually knows how the Feingold diet works, if it does work. Feingold himself thought that some children had an inherited biochemical disorder that made colourings poisonous to many parts of the body. Another theory is based on the known ability of salicylates to block the body's own manufacture of substances called prostaglandins from the raw material – essential fatty acids – in the diet (see below). Prostaglandins are chemicals that control processes in many parts of the body so that a child affected in this way would be expected to have many physical problems. It has been suggested that some people who are deficient in prostaglandins can make up by taking large quantities of fatty acids in the form of evening primrose oil. Even additives (particularly sodium glutamate) are thought by some people to be helpful.

Another theory is that the food additives could affect brain function directly. Obviously, the question of how the diet works is secondary to whether it works at all. If it is effective, most parents will want to use it without waiting for detailed knowledge of what it is truly doing to the brain.

The food allergy theory

A different sort of dietary approach is advocated by clinical ecologists – doctors and scientists who specialize in the adverse reactions to food and other substances in the environment. They suggest that many foods – natural as well as synthetic – can give rise to allergies. In an allergic reaction, the body is damaged by its own immune defences that normally protect it from infection. The white blood cells, which are involved in protecting the body, cannot normally enter the brain, and because of this the medical profession has been reluctant to accept allergy as a cause of neurological and psychiatric problems. But once again, the question of how it works is secondary to that of whether the diet affects children.

Nearly any food can give rise to an allergy; milk, eggs and wheat are among the commonest. Multiple allergies are common.

Sometimes there can be obvious clues for an allergic reaction, for example if your child has a skin rash or asthma. Another suggested clue is that some foods causing allergies also cause the affected person to crave them – so you should be suspicious of favourite foods. Another way of testing for a food allergy is to go on to a radical exclusion diet (or oligoantigenic diet) consisting of a very few, relatively pure foods, and then adding suspected articles of diet one at a time (see page 61).

Dietary deficiencies

Some experts recommend a different kind of diet again – one in which foods that are thought to be lacking in the diet, are added. These include various vitamins, especially pyridoxine, and minerals such as zinc. One theory suggests that giving very large doses of vitamins ('megavitamin therapy') could overcome some unknown deficiency in the body's chemistry.

Do the diets work?

There is a bewildering range of diets for your child to try if you listen to all the experts. Most of the suggestions are not based on evidence, or even on theory, but on speculation.

The main evidence in favour of the treatments is simply the reports of individual children who were very difficult before they were started on a special diet and much easier to manage afterwards. Several of these children have been written about, often by their parents.

Unfortunately, this evidence is not always good enough. When a diet is started, many other things change and must be taken into account. For example an atmosphere of hope is created and children are expected to start to improve.

These subtle pressures and expectations can have very powerful influences on children. They are seen in research studies of drug treatment that substitute an active tablet with a dummy tablet or placebo that contains no drug, but looks exactly the same as the active treatment. All these studies find that the psychological effect of taking a treatment is strong enough to make a substantial difference to some children even if the tablets are placebos. I remember one mother talking about her son, who had started treatment: 'It's a miracle – this is really a cure – he is a different boy entirely.' In fact he was taking a dummy tablet. Optimism and encouragement are good for children, and the real, physical effect of diets needs to be disentangled from them as with the effects of pills.

Scientists have tried to get round this problem by giving a diet in such a way that children and their parents do not know just what their food contains. Obviously this is difficult; people usually know what they are eating! However, it is not impossible, and the Feingold diet has had several careful scientific evaluations.

Testing the Feingold diet

This additive-free diet (see above) has been tested against a 'placebo diet' containing additives to see whether it was really effective for hyperactive children, but the results were inconclusive. A few children may have improved on the Feingold diet but there was also a real possibility that the families knew when they were having the 'active' diet – and this would naturally affect the results. Other trials have been much more elaborate, and researchers have gone to great lengths to disguise the nature of the diet. Each week they provided a different set of foodstuffs for everybody in the family. The results of this trial showed no difference between the Feingold diet and the diets that included the additives.

Researchers then changed their line of attack and tried a different way of testing the diet. They used children who were already on the Feingold diet, many of whom had responded well to it, and gave them cookies or capsules; some contained artificial colourings, others were placebos. The researchers expected the children to become hyperactive again when they ate the food containing colourings, but not when they ate the placebos, even though they were unaware which was which at the time. Several studies done in this way came to a similar conclusion. Children who had responded to a diet without artificial colours, even responded dramatically, did *not* get more hyperactive when the artificial colours were given again. Probably their earlier response was psychological, and not due to the physical effect of the treatment.

This was not quite the end of the story. When the response of individual children was studied, it turned out that an occasional child really did behave much worse when given additives – even though the vast majority of hyperactive children did not.

If this is the true conclusion, and only a few children can be treated successfully with the Feingold diet, then it explains a great deal. It explains why some children seem to do well, and yet why most families coming to my clinic who have tried the diet have been disappointed and distressed by its failure to help. It implies that people should not oversell the diet on the basis of a good personal experience. You will have to decide whether or not to try diets on your child by balancing a low chance of success – it seems only a small fraction of children do well on the diet – against any risks (see page 63).

Some recent scientific work has been done to test the possibility that a wide range of foods – possibly different for each child – can upset the control of attention and behaviour. The evidence is not conclusive yet, but I know of three studies and all of them have come to the same conclusion. A small number of children are helped by an exclusion diet and become more hyperactive when certain foods are added. In the main trials, children go on to an exclusion diet and if they improve new foods are added one at a time until they are eating a balanced diet which excludes the foods that have upset behaviour. At this point, the scientific trial begins. The food, whatever it is, is disguised and given in such a way that the child, the family, and the researcher who is testing the child cannot tell whether the child has had the food or not on any particular day. For instance, if cows' milk is responsible, then on some days the child would have a substitute such as sheep's milk; and on other days the sheep's milk will have added to it a small amount of the cows' milk – too small to detect, but enough to upset behaviour. These studies suggest that, if a child has reacted badly to one particular food, then objective tests carried out by people who do not know what the child has taken, will also show that the food is upsetting the child's activity and attention.

The commonest foods to upset children in this way are quite natural – wheat flour, cows' milk, fruit juices and eggs can all be the substances that provoke a child. Confusingly, what upsets one child will probably not upset another. There is detective work to be done for each child to find out what the responsible causes are.

The best guide to what may be upsetting your child is what you notice yourself. If you keep a diary, you may well be able to see that some particular foods are upsetting him. Alternatively, if there is a food for which he has a special craving, then that may be the one responsible. If you do not see any reaction to particular foods, or if there is nothing that he craves, or if a period of trial with a very strict exclusion diet (see Level C below) does not work; then it is not likely that it will help to go further into diet treatments. There is a danger of distorting a child's nutrition, as ever more foods are eliminated. Drastic alterations to the diet can bring their own hazards. Since the majority of hyperactive children are not helped by a dietary approach, it is better to accept the limitations of that line of treatment and turn to others.

Caffeine   One substance in normal diets known to affect activity levels especially in hyperactive children, is caffeine. This drug is not only present in tea or coffee. It is also added to many soft drinks. A child who drinks many of them in a day may well have taken a dose quite sufficient to alter his psychological functioning. Its effects are complex, and it has been used as a stimulant drug (see page 91) to treat hyperactivity. It probably increases concentration in some children, yet it can also increase the level of activity and certainly produce irritability and tension. It is worth considering caffeine as a possible cause if your child is a 'soft drink addict'.

How to alter your child's diet

Since there are so many different ways of altering the diet, people who decide on this treatment need some kind of strategy. There are several levels of complexity, but most people will probably start with the simplest and then decide whether it is worth working up the scale.

Level A   The simplest and probably the most satisfactory approach will begin with your own observations. If you have noticed that particular foods upset your child, then try to avoid them systematically. This is all the more worthwhile if your child suffers from an allergic illness (such as asthma or skin rashes) which is made worse by certain foods. Artificial food additives, chocolate, milk and fizzy drinks have been the most frequently incriminated foodstuffs. If this diet is having no effect, it should become evident within a few days.

The limitation of this common sense level is that you can only judge the effect of one food at a time. If you find that you are testing one idea after another, and that your child's diet is getting more and more restricted without any major changes in behaviour or learning, then stop. Either look at other ways of helping your child, or go to level C and seek professional supervision.

Level B (for example, the Feingold diet)   The next step is probably the least satisfactory. It involves a 'blind' elimination of foodstuffs on the grounds that they are often implicated as the cause of other children's allergies. It may, however, be worth a try if you are determined to use diet treatment and have no reason to think that anything else is affecting your child.

Since the most common complaints are about artificial food colourings and preservatives, a modification of the Feingold diet would be the most likely to help. This will mean changing your shopping and cooking habits to exclude absolutely everything containing synthetic colouring. Many foods must therefore be avoided and these include:

- All ice cream, ice lollies, sweets, chocolates and chewing gum unless you know that they do not contain additives (for example because they are home made);
- Processed meat, sausage, salami, bacon, ham, pork pies, ready-cooked chicken or turkey, frozen meat and frozen fish – unless it is clear from the labels that they have not been artificially flavoured or coloured;
- Most fizzy drinks (except additive-free fizzy drinks and mineral water), all squashes that have added colouring, all instant breakfast drinks, drink mixes, flavoured yoghurt drinks. Manufacturers should state all additives on the label but if there is no list of ingredients, avoid it;
- All instant and ready-made desserts, jellies, manufactured cakes, pies or dessert mixes, biscuits, jams, preserves and pastries;
- Commercial breakfast cereals, unless they specifically state they do not contain artificial additives;
- Most kinds of wrapped bread (even baker's bread may contain colouring, so you will need to ask if in doubt); margarine, processed or coloured cheese;
- Flavoured potato chips, prepared chips, tomato sauce (unless additive-free), soy sauce, wine or cider vinegar, pickles, salad cream and prepared mustard.

In addition to this long list of foods, you will need to avoid colouring in many other things: for example, vitamin tablets, throat sweets, antacids, mouthwashes, coloured medicines and tablets, and coloured toothpaste. You will find that you need to prepare most meals from fresh food and do most of your own baking. Flour is usually safe, as are fresh meat and vegetables that have not been listed above and have not been coloured. Potatoes, beans, eggs, honey, fruit and home-made sweets are all acceptable in this diet. The original Feingold diet insisted on excluding many fruits because they contain natural salicylates; this seldom makes any difference.

If the diet 'works', then the next step will be to reintroduce some of the eliminated foods, one by one. Remember that the psychological effects of going on a diet are strong, so that any improvement may turn out not to be due to a particular food at all.

For further information on food additives and exclusion diets, see *The Allergy Diet*, a companion volume in this series.

Level C The clearest and most comprehensive way of assessing a diet is by excluding a very wide range of foodstuffs. I only recommend this if done under professional supervision, by a dietitian or by your doctor.

It begins with a very restricted exclusion diet. This may consist of eating a very small number of foods; perhaps two meats (such as chicken and lamb), two fruits (such as apple and banana), two vegetables (such as beans and cauliflower) and one other food (such as potato). If this makes no difference to your child's hyperactivity, then you try another drastic diet, eating two different meats than before, and so on, so that there is no overlap between the two diets. If there is still no improvement, then diet treatment is unlikely to be the solution for your child.

If an exclusion diet is helpful, then the next step is to reintroduce foodstuffs, one at a time. This diet is *not* suitable for long-term use. Its only purpose is to identify which foods give rise to a reaction. It is important to be supervised by your doctor or dietitian because they can help to diagnose the presence of a reaction to a food. Once identified, the trigger foods can be avoided and the diet can otherwise be normal.

It is important to remember that:

- Professional help is very desirable if complex dietary changes are to be made. A hospital dietitian attached to a department of paediatrics may be in a position to help.
- If you go to a specialized private clinic, then get another opinion first.

Do the diets have disadvantages?

Physically speaking, the Feingold diet is pretty safe. If adhered to very strictly, particularly eliminating all fruit from the diet, then vitamin C deficiency could be a risk. But this should be easy to avoid by adding ascorbic acid to the diet. Usually the outcome is a balanced diet.

Diets that eliminate a very wide variety of ordinary foods can become distorted nutritionally. Too much enthusiasm in applying severe restrictions can actually put your child's health at risk. This is particularly unfortunate, because there is really no evidence that extreme restrictions are ever helpful.

The main disadvantage of diet treatments is, however, psychological. Most diets are arduous and time consuming for the person who cooks, and unpopular with the children because many attractive sweets and junk foods are forbidden. Though there can be a big short-term boost to morale in starting, in the longer term they can be a focus for discontent and discouragement. Positive family relationships are so important in treating hyperactivity (see Chapter five) that it is not worth jeopardizing them for anything less than a large benefit.

It can also be very disheartening if a treatment fails after having been enthusiastically recommended and carefully put into practice. There is a real temptation then to give up and neglect other treatments.

If you decide to experiment with the diets, then avoid becoming over involved with them. I have known children to be forbidden to play with other children for fear that they might be given a sweet or candy. In this case the restriction was more damaging than the problem would have been. You should also take care not to become so preoccupied with diets that everything else is neglected. Children with hyperactivity commonly have many needs. The more severe the hyperactivity, the less likely is food to be a dominating consideration. It is all too easy to lose sight of educational or psychological avenues of help amongst the exciting possibilities of physical treatment.

I have tried to point out how very limited the chances are of helping children's hyperactivity by changing their diet. Personally, I don't recommend it routinely. Nevertheless, the scientific evidence for or against diet treatment is inconclusive as yet, so you have to decide for yourself. Your knowledge of your own child is the best guide. If you do decide to try it, I should still like to suggest a few dos and don'ts.

- DO keep a sense of perspective.
- DO consider other kinds of help in addition to diets.
- DO remember that diet is not a last resort. If it fails, there are still plenty of other ways to help your child and you should not despair.

- DON'T enforce a restrictive and distorted diet on your child if the simple things don't work.
- DON'T evangelize about the diet; it may be misleading and distressing to families who have been unsuccessful.

7

Coping with hyperactivity

The general view that I have tried to convey so far is that hyperactivity is not usually a disease but a pattern of problem behaviour. It does not usually have a single cause or a single cure. But there are several things that can be achieved through your relationship with your child before trying the treatment services that I will describe in Chapter nine.

You and your child

There is no one best way of bringing up hyperactive children, any more than there is one right kind of child-rearing generally. Every family works differently, and general rules are generally wrong. You may have been given broad advice about discipline including 'always avoid smacking' or 'never use bribery' or 'never give way to blackmail'. No rule should be followed slavishly. The best guide is simply what works best for you and your child; and on this matter *you* are the expert.

The suggestions that follow are therefore not meant to be rules. They do not replace parental wisdom, and they are certainly not intended to replace any professional advice that has been tailored to your child's individual needs. Rather, they are based on my observations of families who cope well, and the differences that distinguish them from others who cope badly.

The parents whose hyperactive children develop well are often those who survive best themselves.

- They have found ways of identifying and encouraging their child's self control.
- They set up clear rules, and they manage to keep up a lot of shared activities with their child even though there may be clashes as well.
- They manage to be self controlled themselves.
- When there are two parents, they keep a reasonably united approach.
- They may differ greatly in the discipline they apply but, whatever it is, they have thought it out in advance and have been prepared to change it if it does not work out.

Identifying the positive points

No child is totally disorganized. Even the most severely hyperkinetic children spend some time in persistent playing with one toy, or watching television, or doing something they are supposed to do. It may seem a dishearteningly small amount of time, but nevertheless, the key to building it up is recognizing the positive points. This is in some ways an unnatural thing to do.

Take the example of a seven-year-old boy who is 'always' rushing about, who is a whirlwind of activity at mealtimes, and who runs away from the table twenty times during his tea. The 'natural' reaction is to respond to the times that he runs off. However, he must also have come to the table twenty times, and he is very likely to have spent several seconds at it. It is less natural to react to those few seconds of good behaviour – but it is also much more effective.

It is important to base your actions upon your own child, not upon an idealized notion of what a child should be like. This sounds obvious, but again it may not come naturally. The temptation is to compare your son or daughter all the time with his or her brothers and sisters, classmates, or friends. This can be very unhelpful if it leads to being preoccupied with the negative side of your child's behaviour. If you saddle him or her with the remote and difficult goal of being the same as everybody else, the result is discouragement. A much better goal is simply that he or she should do a little better the next week.

It may be very difficult to accept hyperactive children for what they are. Because their behaviour can vary so much from day to day, one feels that they can do much better if only they would try. Correspondingly, it is easy to be frustrated with their lack of progress and get angry with them. Research has suggested, however, that the more critical parents are of the children, the less good is the psychological outcome for the child. It may help, in accepting and living with the very difficult behaviours that can be part of the hyperkinetic syndrome, that it is a medically recognized condition and not simply naughtiness. The changeability from one time to another is part of the disorder, not a sign that your child is 'putting it on'. It is not madness, and many children develop very well in spite of the disability.

A good qualities list   One useful exercise is to write down such a list including the things that you particularly value about your child. You will probably start with things about him or her that seem better than other children, but then go on to other good qualities that could be encouraged. You may well find yourself writing a lot of 'buts': 'she sits down with her books, but then very often she screams that she can't do anything'. If so, rewrite the list without the qualifications.

The aim is to identify positive things that you can recognize and reward immediately. The list opposite was drawn up for a severely hyperkinetic boy of ten, with a mental age of about six years. He did in fact have many kinds of wildly uncontrolled behaviour, he had been suspended from several schools, was shunned by other children, and found it very difficult to settle down to anything. Nevertheless, as the list shows, there were several positive things to say about him too.

Using rewards

When you have identified the positive things that you want to encourage, the next step is to find suitable rewards that can be given when – and only when – your child takes a step in the right direction. Children with severe hyperactivity seem to find it difficult to understand the cause and effect of how their behaviour affects others. They cannot profit from a subtle reward, or from

Good Qualities List

1. He's very friendly when he meets someone.

2. He often bounces in happily from school and plays nicely with his sister or the cat for nearly 5 minutes.

3. He's brave and never cries when he's hurt or teased.

4. He doesn't bear a grudge; if he's in trouble it's all over in 10 minutes.

There are several positive things to say about all hyperactive children. When the positive qualities occur, recognize and reward them immediately.

one that is given a long time after their own action – and for example, ten minutes is a long time. Therefore they particularly need a quick, clear, understandable feedback when they have done something right.

Some parents, like some teachers, find reward schemes an alien idea at first, and even offensive. The whole idea can seem like bribery. After all, shouldn't children learn to 'behave themselves' without being paid for it? If they only do something for a reward, won't they stop as soon as the reward stops? Wouldn't it make them less independent if they are being controlled by other people?

These are strong objections, and I should emphasize that I am not advocating reward schemes as the answer to all the problems of bringing up children, nor to all children's problems. I am simply saying that they seem to be a very useful approach to some of the difficulties entailed by hyperactivity. In this context they are aids to learning, not bribery.

The purpose of bribery is to get people to do something corrupt. The purpose of reward is to encourage development. Everybody needs some sort of recognition for their achievements. Hyperactive children are no different, but find recognition much harder to get. Their growth to independence is usually held back by being disorganized rather than by an excess of control.

The power of attention Reward is not just a matter of giving sweets or pocket money. Rewards like these will probably be useless if they are given out grudgingly with sarcastic remarks and a sour face. Often the biggest reward of all is simply the way the other person reacts.

Attention from a parent is such a powerful need for children that it sometimes outweighs everything else. Often parents intend to punish misbehaviour (for example, by scolding), but find that the supposed punishment actually makes matters worse. This may be because punishing usually involves a great deal of adult attention focussed directly on children. Some children will go to great lengths to get this attention, almost irrespective of whether it is superficially pleasant or unpleasant.

A few children seek punishment for other reasons. They may imagine that they have deserved much worse, or they may be so frightened of unpredictable adult reactions that they prefer to bring about a predictable punishment, of which they feel in control. Whatever the reason, the effect of the adult's reaction may unintentionally keep children trapped in a habit of being provocative.

One way out of this 'trap' is to pursue a plan of actively ignoring the wild behaviour that is intended to get attention. I do not mean that you should passively ignore intolerable behaviour by pretending that nothing has happened. That would simply invite further conflict. Instead, by actively ignoring a piece of outrageous behaviour, you are withdrawing attention immediately.

You might have to walk out of the room, send your child to a quiet place, or merely turn your face away and say, 'I'm not going to talk to you for a minute'. This can be an effective policy if the withdrawal of attention takes place against a background of regular reward. In psychological language, it is called 'time out'; that is, time out from the chance of earning rewards. It usually only needs to be a very short time, perhaps one to three minutes.

The need for simplicity and clarity   The social 'rules' that children have to acquire are often subtle and complex. It is rare for a family or a classroom to operate in complete silence or to tolerate universal boisterous activity. Rather, there are occasions when children are expected to be quieter than at other times, and, as they develop, they learn to follow increasingly complicated codes. Usually these involve conditions, and an understanding of the feelings of other people: for example, 'I need to be quieter after tea when the television is turned on, but I can rush about when my father comes home, unless he has a headache, when I need to be extra quiet.'

Many children with hyperactivity are slow to develop their understanding of subtle social situations. Many have an immature appreciation of how other people feel and react to their behaviour. Whatever the cause, they may need to have things spelt out to them, as if to a younger child.

At one level this means keeping rules as simple as possible. At another level it means that rewards need to be clear and obvious and delivered immediately after they have been earned. And, finally, it means that hyperactive children need to experience some adult consistency if they are to model themselves upon it.

Most adults can appear inconsistent and puzzling to young children, who cannot understand the motives of grownups. You will find it easier to be consistent in discipline if you have explicit rules to work with. It can also take some of the heat out of personal confrontations if there is a rule to which you can resort.

The rules that work best therefore seem to be simple enough for your child to understand and clear enough to be written down (see page 74). They should be put in a positive form so that children can be encouraged to keep them rather than punished for breaking them. For example, 'Leave matches alone' sounds more direct and understandable than 'Don't play with fire when you're on your own'. 'Make your bed in the morning' is much easier to follow than 'Don't make your mother do everything for you, it isn't fair'. The impersonality of more direct rules is less likely to lead to the vicious cycles of hostility and resentment I described in Chapter five.

One step at a time

There is not much point in setting up a scheme of positive expectation and reward if your child never meets your expectations and never earns rewards. It can even do harm by confirming the belief of some children that their efforts are destined always to fail.

Before you begin to use a rules and reward system it is important to start with something relatively easy that is very likely to work. 'If you're very good all the holidays you can have a bicycle' is not likely to be helpful. It sets up a very big reward and a huge, remote goal. This is exactly the kind of rule that hyperactive children find very difficult. By contrast, 'you win ten points for every shop we go into in which you stay by my side' sets up a small but immediate reward for a small advance, and is more likely to help.

Naturally, you must decide what the first step should be. It is usually best to start in easy stages, with a minor problem not with the worst and most upsetting one. This will help you and your child to get a feel for the scheme. When it is working it can then be extended to the central difficulties. To begin with you should concentrate on one problem at a time. Later on, more than one goal can be added.

Try starting the scheme with a kind of behaviour that you want to encourage, and which already happens occasionally. The positive things already identified on a 'good qualities test' are usually a good place to start. For the boy described on page 67, his parents began by extending the amount of time that he played cooperatively, beginning with three minutes (measured with a timer) and giving him plenty of praise and smiles at the end of that time. They then increased the time by thirty seconds a day, and within a few weeks, their son was playing happily for up to an hour on end.

It worked because they could encourage his strength – following an understandable rule for a short time, and avoid his weakness – of not concentrating well enough to hold complex plans for long in his head.

The two important points in this example were:

• The immediacy of the reward which was probably more

important than exactly what form it took.
- The gradual approach. If his parents had demanded an hour of constructive play at the beginning, they would have achieved nothing except demoralization.

Letting off steam

It is usually a mistake to try to achieve permanent calmness in children who are hyperactive. It is asking too much, and excessive constraint may make things worse, as for the boy described on page 54. They need the opportunity to let off steam and get rid of bottled-up energy as much as to learn to control their activity when necessary.

Sometimes it is easy to find gardens and safe places to play in and let off steam. The issue is much harder when circumstances are against you. A small flat in a tower block, for example, makes life enormously difficult. There is probably no good solution to the difficulties when a severely hyperkinetic child is cooped up in this way. It is perfectly reasonable to seek medical advice from your doctor or a specialist, for rehousing in these circumstances. If there is no choice about it, then it may well be the factor that finally persuades a family to seek treatment for their child.

One clever approach was thought up by a single mother, who made a moveable barrier of string to divide the single family living-room in half. For about ten minutes every half hour the barrier was lifted, and her handicapped and hyperactive son was allowed to run riot on one side of the room while she, the other children, the television and the breakables remained on the other side. This scheme had the disadvantage that the other children tended to regard their brother as freakish; but it did allow for twenty-minute spells of normal family life.

At a less extreme level, many parents find it helpful to have regular short periods when children can make as much noise and disturbance as they like in a defined area. If this means that one room in the house is chronically untidy and knocked about, the price is not exorbitant. This 'loud play' can work as a reward for quiet periods.

Thinking developmentally

This chapter has so far sketched out a general approach to managing restless and inattentive behaviour, and will go on to suggest a specific way of putting it into operation. The ideas may or may not be useful to you: they have to be rather general, because every child – and for that matter every parent – is different. You have to translate the advice into your own circumstances.

One of the key considerations when learning to cope with hyperactivity is the developmental level of your child. This means more than just age, because children can develop at different rates. Furthermore, different aspects of a child's development are often out of phase with each other. A child of ten years might have the mathematical ability of a twelve-year-old, be reading at the level of a ten-year-old, yet have the social understanding of an average six-year-old. Parents are generally very sensitive to the maturity of their children, and usually their instincts are a good guide.

Different ages will obviously need different approaches. Again, this means more than pitching goals and expectations at the right level. The whole way that rules operate needs to change from age to age. Thus, a child of four years (or an older child functioning at that level) needs parental authority to be presented with love and firmness.

Children at eight years will need much more reasoning to back up rules. Fairness is a key idea to them and they should be working out self control rather than surrendering themselves to be controlled. The rapidly developing independence of twelve-year-olds means that strict rules and enforced authority are increasingly inappropriate. They need a shift towards negotiated agreements. Rules give way to bargaining, which is a useful skill for older children to learn.

A SCHEME OF GOALS, RULES AND REWARDS

The general ideas of this chapter need to be interpreted in concrete terms for each individual child, but they can be summarized in the following order:

Identify positive goals Goals are the immediate targets for your child to achieve. Good useful goals should be:

- Clear
- Explained in positive terms
- Attainable
- Appropriate to your child's level of development
- Few in number.

Agree rules for rewarding progress When the goal is decided, break down the progress towards it into realistic steps. The aim is to be able to reward each step as it is achieved, and for each step to be small and easy. One good way, already mentioned, is to increase gradually the length of time spent doing something.

Another way is to have several little goals, the overall purpose being to create some time spent in constructive activity. For example, you could begin by watching television with your child for a period, then go on to looking at a picture book together for the same period, and then on to reading to your child for the same time. Particularly difficult behaviour is often best dealt with by withdrawing your attention – the 'active ignoring' method mentioned on page 70.

Reward each step towards the goal Good rewards should be:
- Given immediately
- Pleasant – that is, they should be something actually liked by your child, not what he or she is supposed to like
- Consistent
- Given warmly – that is, with praise and affection. Indeed, praise is often a good enough reward in itself.

When children are old enough, the reward can be delayed by putting a star (or points or a token) on a chart that can count towards a later reward requiring a number of stars. Most children can cope with this by the age of four.

The diagram on page 77 shows an example of a star chart that worked well for a seven-year-old girl with a mental age of about five. The chart was simply ruled on paper and decorated with stick-on stars bought from a stationers. The picture reminded her of what she was supposed to be doing, as she could not read yet. The goal was to go quietly to bed when told; the reward was a star and immediate praise. In addition she could exchange each star for an extra fifteen minutes of television time the following day. When she failed to earn a star, she was quietly and neutrally reminded that she had lost that extra time.

The main advantage of this scheme is that it often works. Nevertheless, you may well decide that such an approach is not for you. Perhaps it seems too complicated to try without help; perhaps things are going well enough already; perhaps it is at odds with your philosophy of bringing up children. In any event, some of the principles can be generally applied. You may not like the idea of systematic, formal rewards, but you should check that you are showing approval and acceptance to your child sometimes, that you share some activities at times, and that you have a planned idea of what you hope your child will learn next.

The examples above have mostly centred around the two major difficulties shown by children with hyperactivity; controlling their concentration and controlling their activity. They are major because many other problems can arise from them. However, these other problems may well be the biggest, and the hardest to deal with.

The next chapter will go on to discuss some problems that can be linked to hyperactivity: not only other behaviour problems, but also some of the complications of family life. The most alarming to parents is the possibility that they may lose their own self control to the point of violence. While these added complications are rather different, they can all happen in children who are hyperactive. Accordingly, the general strategy of positive, simple goals and clear immediate rewards still applies.

Opposite: You can easily draw up a star chart like this for your child. In this example, the child was rewarded with a star and immediate praise if she went quietly to bed, without making a fuss.

GOING TO BED CHART

	Monday	Tuesday	Wednesday	Thursday	Friday	Saturday	Sunday	Total
Week 1	★							1
Week 2			★			★		2
Week 3		★			★			2
Week 4		★	★	★		★		4

Notes: 1 star earns 15 mins watching TV after 7 pm.
1 star earned each time she goes up to bed within 1 minute of being told.

8

Coping with complications

Several kinds of problem behaviour are more common in children who are hyperactive. They are by no means confined to the hyperactive, but they need to be confronted by parents of hyperactive children. These complications follow on after hyperactivity but they may in fact be the most troublesome aspect of an individual's case.

SLEEP PROBLEMS IN YOUNG CHILDREN

Victor, who was described in Chapter two, had one sort of sleep problem – but there are many others. The first step in tackling such a difficulty is to find out the cause. Does it, for instance, represent fear of the dark or of loneliness? Many young children's fears go unrecognized because they cannot express themselves in words. Is it the result of a tantrum at bedtime because your child rebelled against your directions? Or do the rows at bedtime occur because your child is bored and needs less sleep than you and resents being cooped up in his or her room?

You should not simply assume that sleeplessness is part of hyperactivity. As a matter of fact, many severely hyperkinetic children sleep unusually soundly. The first step to coping with sleep problems is therefore to try to analyse why they happen.

The action you take will be determined by what you want to achieve. For instance, it may turn out that your child is getting enough sleep but you are distressed by being interrupted many times a night. The goal then may well be, not to get him to sleep more, but for him to stay and play in his room – and this may be more easily achieved. To think too much about 'hyperactivity' in this context might actually distract you from the process of finding a solution that is right for your child. The word 'hyperactivity' refers to what such children have in common, not to what is unique to each. But the individual qualities are usually the important ones, and that's where you, the parents, are the experts.

Solutions   The commonest solution to sleep problems in practice is for parents to take their child to bed with them. This has obvious disadvantages in keeping parents apart, and sometimes it means that nobody gets much sleep. Another possible solution is to give the child a hypnotic medicine to increase sleep. This has the possible drawback of a hangover the following day, but the usual serious disadvantage is that it does not work for long. It may work for a short time, but the problem often returns. Furthermore, as I have said, increasing the amount of sleep is not always the best idea.

In Victor's case (see page 11) the fight seemed to have become more important than the issue of whether he was sleeping enough. In the event, the problem was largely reduced when his father's patience snapped; he took over the disciplining of bedtime and forcibly marched Victor back to his room in grim silence. At the same time, both parents agreed that he could keep his light on, and stocked the room with his toys.

After a couple of weeks, Victor was staying cheerfully in his room. The boy seemed to be relieved by his father's decisive action, and indeed no new problems appeared. All this happened around the time of referral for treatment, so no specific therapy was involved. Rather, the story illustrates how individual and personal coping can sometimes be hampered by an idea that a behaviour difficulty must be the result of an illness.

Checklist for sleep problems

It is worth thinking through a checklist of the different stages at bedtime that cause problems.

- **Going to bed**   If the issue is a fight over bedtime, then the same kind of principles may hold that were applied to learning new skills (see page 40). Could the fight itself be rewarding through the attention and excitement involved? If so, going to bed on time becomes a habit to learn, in gradual steps, through rewards. Tantrums about going to bed may be susceptible to the same techniques as tantrums in general (see opposite).

- **Settling into bed**   Settling down for the night involves a big change of pace, which may be hard for restless children to achieve on their own. If they do not already have a ritual for bedtime, it is worth creating one. A very regular pattern of goodnights – teeth cleaning, story and tucking up, for example – is likely to be reassuring and also a strong sign for the change of tempo. Most children evolve their own rituals (which may reach inordinate lengths unless checked by an adult); many hyperactive children do not.

  Being left alone at night is also a worry for some children, and it may drive them to pester adults or other children for company. If so, as with other childish fears, encourage your child, firmly and calmly, to master the fear rather than indulge in it. A quiet and matter-of-fact return to bed may have to be repeated many times when you start it but should become progressively easier over successive evenings.

- **Staying in bed**   It is reasonable to expect children to stay in bed even if they do not fall asleep for some while. A night light and plenty of quiet activities and toys to play with may help to keep a wakeful child cheerful.

- **Waking up and getting up**   Is this because of nightmares or night terrors? If so, consider whether any general sources of stress need to de dealt with. Is it because getting up is followed by something rewarding? If the result is excitement, or an argument, or getting into the parents' bed, then no wonder it carries on. Aim again for a matter-of-fact and calm return, even if this needs to be repeated frequently at the beginning. If there are screams and tantrums on returning, then try the 'withdrawal of attention' treatment (see page 70).

- **Short hours of sleep**   Is it just that your child does not need much sleep? If so, aim to ensure that he or she is constructively occupied though alone. If the issue becomes your exhaustion, then consider taking shifts if there are two of you, or even trying a sleeping drug yourself.

  Could it be due to treatment? If your child is one of those who needs to go on the stimulant drug treatment in Chapter nine, then sleeplessness is a recognized effect of the treatment. It may mean that the dose is too high; discuss it with your doctor. Alternatively, if a sleeping drug has been prescribed at night, then the wrong dose may make a young child 'fighting drunk' and even less likely to get to sleep. Again, it needs to be discussed with your doctor.

TANTRUMS

Most toddlers throw tantrums, and doing so is a part of normal development. Children's growing independence virtually requires that there will be clashes with adult authority. Hyperactive children tend to have more tantrums than others. Their restlessness brings them more frequently and more intensely into clashes with grownups.

The first step in coping with a child whose rages are extreme and frequent is, just as with sleeping difficulties, to think through why they are happening. They are often a kind of language – they are communicating something important about the child. Their function in communication may be all the stronger if a delay in development makes it harder for a child to communicate his needs through ordinary words.

Since hyperactive children often have delays in language – and those who do not are still prone to more subtle delays in social understanding – it is all the more necessary for adults to try to articulate their problems for them. Illness, pain, insecurity, fear – all make inarticulate children lash out at those who are closest to them.

Tantrums are a part of normal development and not a sign of hyperactivity.

The second step in coping with rages is to avoid, when reasonable, the circumstances that bring them about. However, there is a distinction that needs to be drawn. It can be helpful to recognize when an unnecessary confrontation is looming and skirt around it with humour. It can store up trouble if you also skirt around necessary confrontations to the degree of allowing or encouraging outrageous behaviour. Chapter five has already outlined the need to take a middle stance.

The third step in handling tantrums is to organize what happens as a result of them. Chapter seven has sketched out one useful general approach. Parents' immediate actions are often dictated by the goal of making sure the tantrum ends with nobody hurt. This sometimes means physically holding children who are out of control, so that they can feel control being restored. In addition, however, your actions need to make future tantrums less likely. It is therefore important that children do not get a reward from you because of the tantrum.

Sometimes the reward will have been the enforcement of their own will, which means of course that they should not have that particular wish indulged – or not, at any rate, because of the tantrum. Sometimes they will have been getting attention from it (see Chapter seven). If this seems to be the case, then the immediate handling of the temper ought to be guided by the principle of giving as little attention as possible. Often it is possible to 'exile' a child into the bathroom or another safe place for a few minutes or until they calm down. Their act of calming down can then be praised and rewarded. Even if this is impossible – because children have to be physically controlled in the interests of safety – they can still be held facing away from the adult taking care of them.

Violent and disruptive tantrums may be a bigger problem with older children. The worst way of reacting to them is with anger and violence. This makes more aggression from the children virtually certain in the long run. Self-willed violence may indeed need to be punished; but the withdrawal of reward is a better way of doing it. The 'active ignoring' described on page 70 may very well need to be extended to a short period on their own – until they then calm down. This should be away from the attention rewards that they are probably getting from parental shouting or fighting, and away from the warmth and praise (or the more material rewards) that will come once they are controlled again.

If you adopt this kind of approach, then do not expect a sudden change. You will probably find, when the policy of withdrawing attention starts, that there is a spell of a few days or weeks when tempers become more frequent and intense in the quest for the missing reaction. If you can nevertheless persist, then the tempers should gradually become 'unlearned' and start to disappear. The older your child, the more difficult this is likely to be, and the more likely that you will need to seek treatment (see Chapter nine).

- Avoid letting your child see people he or she respects act violently. Try not to be violent yourself, and keep violent videos away from them.

- Avoid letting tantrums and tempers win. If they achieve their purpose then of course they will stop for a while – but they will be more likely to happen again.

A dependent child

Immature children naturally need things done for them. Parents' actions can either encourage them to be more independent or keep them in a regressed and baby-like set of habits.

Marian had suffered a mild form of cerebral palsy (partial paralysis of the legs) from birth. It made her rather clumsy and her short attention span caused her to fall behind in her learning and need to go to a special school some distance from her home. Mornings were miserable for both her mother and herself, because she was so slow getting dressed and ready for the bus. Her subsequent and frequent lateness for school caused a number of arguments.

Her single mother felt miserable that lack of money made it impossible to de everything she would like for Marian. She had reacted by indulging her daughter in many small ways to make up for the lack. Indeed, she had dressed Marian herself up to the age of nine, but then she felt very strongly that it was time the girl should do this by herself. In the morning Marian would sit on the edge of the bed, dawdling, until her mother came back into the bedroom and scolded her for how little progress she had made. Mother would then go to get on with preparing breakfast, and return to find that only another sock had been put on. She scolded again, and so the cycle went on. Eventually she had to give up, under time pressure, and dress Marian herself.

Marian was only getting attention for her slowness and therefore for her dependence. She was effectively training her mother to nag more and more and therefore to feel worse about it. Conversely, her mother's attention was training her to be slower and slower.

The way out of this was a shift to recognizing and praising small achievements. Instead of criticizing the failures when she came into the room, Marian's mother made herself warmly praise the first steps – even the single sock that had been managed before attention wandered. Marian felt more competent, and did more, and so made an advance towards independence. Even complicated skills, such as tying shoelaces, can be learned in this way provided they are broken down into small stages and each stage is rewarded as soon as it is achieved.

A bored child

Some children with hyperkinesis find it difficult to occupy themselves. They play with many things superficially, but not in a settled way. Others have one or two things that they enjoy, but play with them in a repetitive and even a ritualistic way to the exclusion of everything else; for example, playing with running water for hours.

Hyperkinetic children are unusually dependent upon the outside world for stimulation and interest. If an adult can take the initiative, and keep them occupied with activities and toys, they may be happier while it lasts – but no parent could keep that going all day. Novelty and change in their toys help to sustain interest, and can be partly achieved by joining a toy library. Variety can also be achieved by a place in a day nursery or a stimulating playgroup.

At less severe levels of hyperactivity, television and video games can be a resource as well as a 'drug'. Moderate quantities seem to help build up concentration, at least in the early stages of the process. On the other hand, the vulnerability of hyperactive children to aggressive reactions seems to argue against much exposure to television violence.

Playing with microcomputers is sometimes recommended as a kind of teaching aid. This is often difficult for the severely hyperkinetic, but for the mildly hyperactive it has an important virtue. Some children turn out to be skilful at programming even though they have been 'failures' in ordinary school subjects. If so, they can achieve an experience of success and status in the eyes of others.

Accidents

Reckless exploration can put children at danger. They fall off things and tumble over with alarming regularity. Fortunately, most of these accidents involve no more than minor cuts and bruises – though they may well be serious enough to need a hospital visit.

It is very difficult to protect hyperkinetic children by teaching them about safety, because they tend to be so impulsive in what they do that they do not remember what they have learned. When there is one major danger – for example, a road – then it may be possible to enforce a simple and consistent rule. On the other hand, to restrict them too much carries the opposite risk of protecting them from experiences they need to have if they are to learn. Sometimes parents just have to accept a calculated risk. However, hyperactive children are mainly at risk from minor accidents rather than life-threatening ones. Major accidents are a function of the environment more than of the particular child.

Some risks, however, are unnecessary because they can be guarded against. Electricity wall sockets should be covered over to prevent children pushing wires into them; and there should be no socket near enough to the bathroom to plug in a live appliance. If there are medicines in the house, then it is worth going to extreme lengths to lock them away from the children and to keep them in childproof containers, which chemists provide. Indeed, so far as possible, medicines should be kept out of the house altogether; for example, by returning all unused tablets to the chemist at the end of a course. Too many deaths have proved that a high bathroom cabinet is no barrier at all to a large child with the impulsiveness of a toddler.

Battering and violence to children

Many parents seek help because they have reached a stage of helpless anger and fear that they may do their child some injury. That nightmare haunts many other parents who do not seek help – sometimes because of the greater fear of what that help will involve. The shame they will endure, or the fear that their child will be taken away into care, deters many. Some do indeed go on to injure, or even (rarely) to kill their children.

Those parents who do seek help in these circumstances do not find that their children are automatically removed. On the contrary, professional workers understand very well how people can get into this situation, and their first goal is to help sort out the problems. They may well set up some scheme of supervision if they feel there is a real risk; but this can come as a relief. They know that the vast majority of parents who come forward in this way can indeed be helped.

Help can take many forms, depending upon what is needed. In the context of this book, it might include the recognition of a child's difficulty and setting up a scheme to modify it. It would almost certainly involve other kinds of counselling as well, which are there to act as a support.

There are several avenues to professional advice in these circumstances. In Britain, voluntary help organizations and the local authority department of the social services will have an emergency number in the telephone directory. In North America and Australia, the range of agencies providing help is wider. For some, however, these services are the last resort because of the fear that their child will be taken away into care. They may find it easier to go to their health visitor or family doctor. The next step will probably be a referral to a child guidance unit or a hospital paediatrics' department. I've listed the addresses and telephone numbers of useful organizations at the back of the book.

9

Treating hyperactivity

In the previous chapter I stressed that there need be no shame in deciding that outside help is needed. The organization of professional services is very different in different parts of the world, and they vary in their accessibility and the service they provide. For this reason, no single treatment plan applies.

Clinics (see page 90) will chiefly offer the kinds of treatment in which they are most skilled, for example family therapy. If you have a choice, then you will probably want to go to the centre that can offer several different kinds of approach and help. Otherwise, it is useful to remember that an individual's problems can often be helped by any of several different routes.

Specialized clinics and assessments

Since no one discipline can offer all the kinds of assessment and treatment that may be required, psychological services are usually based upon small teams of professionals working together. The functions of each profession overlap, especially in the provision of psychological schemes of treatment; but each has a core of special expertise.

Child psychiatrists are medically qualified doctors, who have had experience in adult as well as child psychiatry. Their advanced training has been in the psychological disorders of children. These medically qualified people can prescribe drugs, but most spend the majority of their time in psychotherapeutic treatments (that is, treatment through the relationship formed either between doctor and family or play between doctor and child). Child psychiatrists are likely to be involved when a child's problems amount to a definite illness. But they do not confine themselves just to serious cases.

Clinical psychologists have studied the science of psychology and taken a further qualification in its application to health problems. They have specialized knowledge in psychological testing (for example, IQ), and in either psychotherapy or behaviour therapy (see page 97) as well; but many extend their range to include different forms of treatment.

Educational psychologists have a background both in psychology and in teaching, and have taken a higher qualification in the application of psychology to the way children function at school. They are particularly likely to be of help to you if school problems are prominent – especially if your child needs extra educational resources such as a special school or class.

Social workers have a qualification in social work, and the traditional core of their expertise lies in counselling parents and in helping to ensure that children receive adequate care. They may, depending upon how they are employed, have additional legal responsibilities and become involved if a child is to be received into the care of a local authority. However, they also have an extended range of functions. For example, they may counsel you and your child together and their involvement is far more likely to be as a therapist than as an official.

Paediatricians are medically qualified doctors who have specialized in child health, especially physical health. In addition, some have specialized in children's disorders of learning and behaviour and may therefore be involved at any stage.

Psychotherapists have qualified in one particular type of psychotherapy (see page 99); they may have other professional qualifications as well.

The core of a specialized team has to be able to liaise with other professions as well. These include: teachers and remedial teachers; speech therapists; audiologists (who assess and advise about hearing problems); dietitians; art and drama therapists; occupational therapists; nurses and many others.

Access to all this specialized expertise is of course desirable. It is not available everywhere. Even if it is, it can sometimes cause problems in communication between professional services and create difficulties as well as solutions.

Treatment at a clinic

Communication within a clinic is usually achieved by having regular meetings with the various members of the team. They will discuss their patients at such meetings, and these confidential discussions mean that several kinds of expertise can be brought to bear on one child. It often helps these discussions if staff members can see and talk to the families who are being treated.

You may therefore be asked, when you attend a clinic, if other professional people can be present at your interview. This may involve sitting in a room with a one-way mirror behind which other professionals are sitting. They may ask to make a videotape recording of your interview. You do not have to agree to such a setting if you do not want to. However, it is usually to your advantage to agree: confidentiality is very carefully maintained and will be explained to you if you ask.

Confidentiality   It is well worth while discussing confidentiality at an early stage. It is an important consideration for many families – for example, who will know about your attendance? In general, professions have a duty to keep whatever you say within confidence – and this can only be overridden by a pressing and immediate need for a child's safety. However, it is nearly always in your child's interest, and therefore your own, if specialized professionals are allowed to consult with others, such as teachers, who are also involved.

The potential difficulties of communication also mean that there should be one professional person who knows everything that is going on and has the power to coordinate, or even to prevent, the interventions of specialists. In Britain, this person should be your family doctor. In North America and Australia it will be your child's paediatrician. With the help of all these other specialists he or she should be in a good position to offer advice.

For this reason, it makes sense that you should first see your family doctor or paediatrician who will then refer you on to specialized services if need be. Many psychiatric clinics will in fact take referrals much more widely, for example from teachers and social workers, and some operate a walk-in policy.

Nevertheless, the best route is usually through primary health care (that is, through your doctor, health visitor or paediatrician). Maybe the advice you get will be that specialized treatment is not desirable. If so, the advice should be carefully considered before deciding on your next course of action.

Physical methods of treatment

Treatment with drugs is probably the most powerful therapy available for hyperactivity. But its very power makes many people wary of it. I shall therefore describe it in more detail than other methods. Not many centres use the drug treatments in Britain, whereas it is the commonest sort of treatment in North America. If it is suggested to you, you may well want to ask many questions:

What are the physical treatments? The commonest treatment involves the use of a stimulant drug such as dextroamphetamine, methylphenidate or pemoline. It may at first sound very surprising that a stimulant should be helpful to an overactive child! The effect was first discovered by accident, but it is not as absurd as it may seem. These drugs are usually thought to stimulate parts of the brain that have previously been under-functioning, so that the result might well be normal behaviour. The purpose of the treatment is to allow children to have better control of themselves and to concentrate more effectively.

In some ways, the word 'drug' treatment is misleading because it suggests that people are being 'drugged' – that is, quietened or tranquillized. Tranquillizing drugs such as diazepam and chlordia-zepoxide are usually given to calm down disturbed and excited

adults. But they offer little help to hyperkinetic children; sometimes they may make affected children even more unstable and less
able to concentrate. For these reasons they are seldom used. The
goal of medication is normally to restore function, not to subtract
anything from a child's mental ability.

Besides the stimulants and the tranquillizers, a third group of
drugs is sometimes recommended. This is the class of 'neuroleptics'
or 'major tranquillizers'. In high doses, these drugs are used to treat
adult mental illnesses. Chlorpromazine and haloperidol are two of
these substances, and they are sometimes prescribed in low doses
to treat hyperkinesis.

How do drugs work?   Amphetamine, a stimulant drug, is very
similar in its chemical composition to some of the substances that
occur naturally in the brain and that take part in the brain's normal
working – particularly noradrenaline and dopamine. These substances are both used by nerve cells to transmit messages to other
nerve cells.

Most researchers think that stimulant drugs, such as amphetamine, work by helping nerve cells in the brain to transmit messages
to other cells. The overall effect is usually to allow hyperactive
children to concentrate for longer periods and, in keeping with
this, to be more in control of themselves. They are therefore quieter
in situations that demand quietness.

Researchers are finding it difficult to work out how the chemistry of the brain affects, and is affected by, mental life. The
uncertainty is even greater with 'neuroleptic' drugs. At the time of
writing, nobody has been able to test fully the idea that imbalances
in transmitter substances normally produced by nerve cells are part
of the causes of hyperactivity. More research is necessary in all
these areas, but even now the action of stimulant drugs is not a
complete mystery.

Sometimes, of course, the drug treatment does not work at all.
Occasionally it is counter-productive, and can make a child more
tense or irritable. But usually the effect is helpful – especially for
times when children are in structured education, such as school.
Sometimes the immediate benefit is spectacular, and children are
able to develop their potential much more fully. These helpful
actions usually occur in children with severe hyperkinesis who

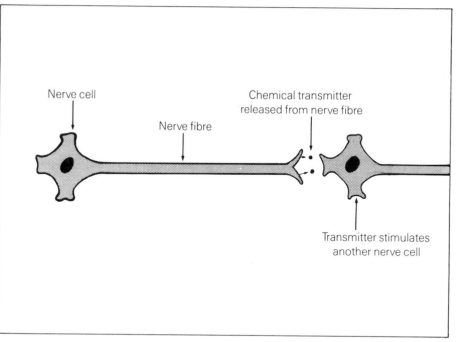

Nerve cell

Nerve fibre

Chemical transmitter
released from nerve fibre

Transmitter stimulates
another nerve cell

How a message passes down a nerve. Most researchers think that stimulant drugs work by helping nerve cells in the brain to transmit messages to other cells, and in so doing, may help the child to concentrate for longer periods.

have most difficulty in concentrating. Teachers, therefore, may see a bigger result than parents.

What are the risks of physical treatments?   The most worrying idea about treatment with stimulant drugs is the fear that children might become dependent upon them. In fact this virtually never happens. The opposite is much more common – that is, the good effect wears off after a period so that medication then needs to be stopped.

Amphetamines are certainly drugs which can be abused, but this is not the case for hyperactive children who use them as part of medical treatment. They do not give children a 'high', and children do not feel more cheerful as a result of taking a dose. On the contrary, a few children feel quite unhappy and tearful when they start to take the medicine, so that the treatment has to be stopped.

I cannot explain why hyperactive children are so different from adult abusers of the drug. Perhaps it has a different effect upon them. Perhaps the small amount of drug prescribed for children is the explanation. Perhaps it is due to the way the drug is explained and presented to the children. Whatever the reason, the main point is clear. Children taking stimulants are not made into addicts.

If these drugs are prescribed for your child, they still have to be treated with care.

- Do not allow them to fall into the hands of other people who might sell them or take them in large doses.
- All drugs should be locked away safely and destroyed when the course is finished. This applies with extra force to all the amphetamine-type drugs.

There are other potentially bad effects of drug treatment, as there are with virtually any medical treatment. Some children develop headaches, some go off their food, and some sleep badly at night. If any of these appear, then you should tell your doctor. They are not signs of any damage being done, but they may well be signs that the dose is too high for your child. Individuals vary greatly in the amount they require, so you may well find that the dose is changed several times in the first weeks of treatment to find the best level. You will also find that the doctor makes regular checks on your child's physical condition.

The dangers of drugs should not be exaggerated. To put them into perspective, the effect of a stimulant drug is comparable in many ways to drinking several cups of coffee a day. The reason that the drugs are prescribed, rather than tea or coffee, is simply that they are safer as well as more effective. They do not have as many side-effects and they do not have so much of a tendency to increase agitation (see Chapter six).

The chief danger of a drug is rather more complicated. It carries the risk that children who take it might come to believe that their successes are because the drug is good, not because they are doing well themselves. It is a misfortune if children come to feel that they are not responsible for their actions. However, this kind of risk needs to be balanced against the risk of not giving the drug, for it can be even worse for a child to grow up under the failures and rejection that hyperactivity entails.

Your attitude as parents can therefore be very helpful if your child does need medical treatment. You should try to convey the understanding that he or she has a problem that is not due to laziness or naughtiness; that medicine is a kind of support which will help your child to overcome that kind of handicap; and that medicine only helps the fight – it does not win it alone.

It is also very helpful if you can communicate the message that there is nothing freakish about requiring drug treatment; it does not mean that your child has a damaged brain or a handicap for life.

How long must physical treatments continue?

There is no one rule about the length of treatment; it varies considerably from child to child. Quite often a good response to treatment allows other things to happen. For example, psychotherapy and behaviour modification (see page 97) can start to have an impact, education can become much more rewarding, and a 'virtuous cycle' can develop in which children start to succeed, feel better about themselves, and gather self-confidence. When this happens, medication can be stopped quite soon (perhaps after six months). Sometimes, however, it is not possible to stop so soon. The drugs are not a cure, but a way of suppressing some troublesome symptoms. If they do need to be continued, it will not be forever.

The normal course of child development will lead to the maturation of at least some of the abilities required for concentration and self-control. It is then unnecessary to treat the problem with drugs. Drug treatment can be seen as a way of preventing the scars that would otherwise result from the period of immaturity. In my experience it is unusual for this treatment to have to continue beyond the age of puberty.

Is there any alternative to drug treatment?

Although the medicines that I have described are probably the most powerful ways of modifying severely inattentive behaviour, they are by no means the only ways. You will probably have tried some of the other ways by the time you attend a specialist clinic.

There is a good deal of variation in methods of treatment between areas and countries. Some regard drugs as the very last resort, some as the front line of treatment. Because of this difference, it follows that parental wishes (and to a lesser extent the wishes of children) should be respected. You can expect to find that any doctor advising medication will be glad to discuss with you the pros and cons in your child's individual case. In particular, you will probably want to ask whether he or she considers that medication is essential to allow psychotherapy, behaviour modification or education to proceed, or whether it is reasonable to delay the decision until other methods have been tried.

In addition, you may want to ask about your doctor's attitude to dietary treatments. Professional approval is not essential for the simpler diets (see Chapter six) but you should certainly seek medical approval or the advice of a dietitian if you contemplate any of the extreme diets that give a very restricted range of foods (see page 55). Professional supervision can also be useful to you in deciding whether a particular diet is helpful or not – for instance, by adding or removing suspected substances one at a time. If medication is to be prescribed, then you should let your doctor know if your child is on any other treatment at the same time.

BEHAVIOUR MODIFICATION

It is less easy to describe psychological therapies (based on discussion, advice and persuasion) that modify behaviour than physical ones, because they are naturally more individual, and will be planned differently for each child. A clinical or educational psychologist (see page 89) usually carries out the treatment. But a member of another discipline (such as psychiatry or social work) may also be trained in these techniques and be able to supervise treatment.

Stages of treatment

Treatment will probably begin with what is called a functional analysis of the problems. This will entail quite detailed questioning, and perhaps observation – watching events at school or at home.

The result is a full description of the history or antecedents of the behaviour problem, the behaviour itself, and the consequences of the behaviour. This scheme is called the 'A-B-C' scheme (for 'antecedents-behaviour-consequences') and is an elaboration and extension of the kind of common sense analysis advocated in Chapter seven.

The analysis will lead on to a treatment scheme. This too may be similar in general form to the goal and reward system of Chapter seven. The detail, however, makes a substantial difference. You will probably be involved in making systematic measurements of particular sorts of behaviour, so as to be clear whether or not the treatment plan is on the right lines.

Behaviour therapy can be direct or indirect.

- **Direct treatment** means that the therapist will treat your child him- or herself. It is like a very systematic form of one-to-one teaching.
- **Indirect treatment** means that you or your child's teachers are trained to carry out behaviour modification. This may mean reading manuals or attending groups. It will certainly mean practising the techniques with your child under supervision.

Psychotherapy on the individual child may involve talking, playing or drawing, but your child's relationship with the therapist will be a major treatment tool.

Behaviour therapy can also be based either upon external rewards and punishments, or upon self-control.

The self-control techniques are promising, at least for children with mild hyperactivity. The treatment involves sessions in which children learn to motivate themselves and run their own systems of reward. The children also learn to think up plans for solving problems.

Impulsive children usually leap to the first and most obvious conclusion – which is often wrong. In academic learning this means a wrong answer. In social learning it means getting into trouble or being unpopular. Such children are taught to give themselves time to think and to work out what kind of problem it is that they are trying to solve. In general, this approach works better with intellectually bright children.

TREATMENT BY UNDERSTANDING (PSYCHOTHERAPY)

Another type of therapy tries to help children to understand their own difficulties. It must be said that it is not a sufficient treatment by itself for most hyperactive children. It may, however, be helpful for some of the emotional problems that have resulted from years of living at odds with other people. It may also help when the problem isn't 'hyperactivity' but a tense, scared agitation based upon bottled-up worries.

If individual sessions of treatment are started, they will be pitched to your child's developmental level. They may involve talking, playing or drawing but, in any event, your child's relationship with the therapist will be the major treatment tool. It may therefore need to be confidential. You should not feel excluded if this is the case. It reflects an attempt to make treatment effective.

Some practitioners base their work upon interview sessions in family therapy, which are attended not only by the child and his or her parents but also by all members of the family; that is, other brothers and sisters. This therapy is particularly likely to be recommended if the assessment has suggested that tensions in family life are creating problems. It is not likely to form the whole of the treatment unless assessment has suggested that there is no serious handicap in your child's own development.

Chapter five described how the attitudes and actions of other people could lead a vulnerable child either towards or away from aggression and antisocial conduct. The opportunity to reduce tensions through discussions with a therapist can therefore be of real value. Such discussions are a very personal matter. I will not describe details, for they will be different for every therapist and for every family.

In summary, professional services involve several different treatment approaches. Some or all of them may be the most relevant to your particular situation. The more complex the problem is, the more likely that several different professionals will be involved. Admission to a hospital ward or day centre or a residential treatment unit is the most intense way of delivering the help of a team. But most clinics base their work upon helping children in their real-life situations and this is usually the home environment or at school.

10

Living with hyperactivity

Sometimes hyperactivity is severe, handicapping and seemingly unmanageable. You may have done your best; specialists may have done their best; and indeed your child may have tried as hard as anybody could; yet difficulties persist.

In this situation you will need to keep in touch with professionals (see page 88) who can keep you informed about what help is available. You will probably wish for this even if their direct treatments do not help much. You should also keep in touch with other parents in a similar situation. If not, look around for groups of parents of mentally handicapped children or of hyperactive children (see page 114).

What will the future bring?

The course of hyperactivity depends partly on its severity, but even more upon whether complications arise. If the main disability is a learning disorder, then it is important to make sure that the right amount of educational help is provided, and to sustain your child's morale by doing everything possible to ensure that his strengths can lead to some successes.

If the main disability is increased alienation, aggression or delinquency then you may need to take a very hard and painful look at whether the whole family has to make big changes – even to alter the whole way your family relates to one another. If your child is in trouble with the law, then you may find yourself having to consider whether he or she is beyond your control and needs to live with others.

Growing up with hyperactivity

The severe problems mentioned above only arise in a few cases so it should be helpful to know something of how most hyperactive children turn out – particularly children whose hyperactivity has been severe enough to need specialist treatment. For many such children, probably about half, their difficulties steadily lessen as they learn other ways round the obstacles they have encountered. There is no magic point at which this happens, and it is not necessarily specifically related to puberty. Rather, there is gradual improvement over a time scale of a few years.

For the less fortunate half, adolescence is a stormy time – but the storm does not usually amount to actual mental illness. Their schooldays are often the unhappiest days of their life. The demands of school are very hard to reconcile with being restless and inattentive. Such children may find a rather free and easy educational approach more appropriate. They might not learn as much as they should, but by the same token they might not be driven so far into frustration and alienation. Having said this, many adolescents with severe problems manage to do as well as anybody else. So the presence of problems does not automatically mean a bad outcome.

In the late teens and early adult life the outcome is considerably better. This is partly because people develop and mature. Indeed, for some of the most handicapped and extremely active, like Simon in Chapter two, there is a reversal in their activity level. They may become rather underactive, and even lethargic, and it may be hard to engage and sustain their attention. At this point it may be necessary to think in terms of how they can best be interested and motivated. A day centre with plenty of change and activities then becomes an important resource.

The better outcome in adult life is also the result of more tolerance in the adult world. There are jobs in which you can be your own master, and go your own way. The determination and independence of some people with hyperactivity then become strengths – especially if they have a basic ability and normal intelligence. Of course, if they have other handicaps, this may stand as an extra obstacle to becoming independent.

It is important to remember that only a minority of hyperactive children – even of severely hyperactive children – are psychiatrically disabled in their adult life. It is well worth persisting with the burdens of trying to help.

Nevertheless, the difficulties of living with hyperkinesis are not to be spoken of lightly. The burden of care can be great, and may need to be shared. Excessive self-sacrifice by some parents can be truly unproductive. Mothers, in particular, have isolated themselves from their communities, neglected their own responsibilities, and shouldered a cross alone. Occasionally they have cracked under that strain, and then everybody is the loser.

You do have to take calculated risks. For example, allow your child to be looked after by other people for short periods – even if this means short holidays away or in a children's home. Your other children need attention, and so does your marriage. This means that you must settle for something less than perfect among specialist teachers and child care staff, and be prepared to stand back a little and relinquish some control of your child's development. All teenagers need some degree of freedom to make their own mistakes. This is harder to give to a hyperactive or handicapped teenager – but no less necessary.

What happens when parents can no longer cope?

The fear of a child being put in a home or another institution haunts many parents – especially when the parents are ageing and the children are severely handicapped. In the past, hyperkinesis in severely retarded people has been a potent reason for long-term hospital admission. This does not need to be the policy. Small, friendly homes and hostels can adequately care for even the very severely affected. Indeed, they can be sufficiently stimulating and secure to make behaviour problems become less prominent. The emptiness of the days in large hospital facilities with few resources can itself make their inmates unoccupied, restless – and, in a word, hyperactive.

RESEARCH AND PROGRESS

The future should also bring new opportunities for treatment and prevention. Obviously, nobody can predict whether breakthroughs will appear. However, current research promises some advances. In several countries, a great deal of effort is going into the best ways of grouping and classifying the problems of hyperactive people. This should lead to a clearer fundamental understanding of the problem, and fewer arguments over words that still confuse parents, teachers and children.

Another important line of research is the patient evaluation of different kinds of treatment, one after another, both separately and in combination. This kind of investigation makes the limitations and strengths of any one treatment more apparent. It highlights what new therapies need to achieve and therefore makes it easier to develop them.

Therapy will also be improved by a clearer and richer understanding of the exact nature of the disabilities from which hyperactive children suffer. Yes, their attention is poor – but what precisely does that mean? Yes, they tend to be isolated and unpopular among other children – but what do they need to learn to avoid being left out? Several groups of researchers are therefore trying to describe the problems as carefully as possible, and to determine how they change during child development. Clearer knowledge of what helps some children to survive unscathed might give clues about how to help all affected children.

Other investigations could give us the clues about what goes wrong in brain function. Studies using brain imaging, investigations of brain chemistry, the electrical workings of the brain, the effects of brain damage in animals, and the genetic basis of the disorder – all these are in progress. The research needs to be supported both morally and financially. We do not by any means have all the answers yet and a better basic understanding about the nature of the condition could be the best way of generating new and more helpful treatments.

I have tried to base this book upon the findings of scientific studies. I have purposefully simplified to a point where some readers will want to challenge dogmatic statements and others will want to study some aspects in depth. If so, the list of further readings at the end of this book contains references that will lead as far into the large scientific literatures as you care to go.

For now, the difficulties of individual children and families are more complex than can be understood by the simple idea of hyperactivity. It is still important to recognize it when appropriate, to cope with it as far as one can and seek treatment when necessary.

You should rely more on your understanding of your child than on any one medical or psychological account, and be a little sceptical about all 'expert' literature on the subject – even this book!

11

Questions and answers

The questions and answers in this section also serve as a summary of the book. They are based on questions frequently asked by children as well as by parents.

What is hyperactivity?

It is a lasting style of behaviour. Affected children seem disorganized and chaotic. They do not persist at activities as long as the vast majority of children of their own age, and they are much more distractible. By the same token, they are restless and tend to act on impulse – so they often end up in trouble or danger.

However, many children are very active, and even 'overactive', without being inattentive or uncontrolled: these children should not be considered to have a psychological disorder. Furthermore, some children who behave inattentively do so only with one person, or only in one place. There is usually nothing wrong with their development.

This book is mostly about children whose attentiveness and restlessness is obvious in all situations, and who are therefore held back from learning and making friends. I think that they have a subtle handicap in the development of attention and self-control that often goes unrecognized. Some have other, more obvious kinds of handicap as well (see Chapter one).

Does hyperactivity go on forever?

Most hyperactive children will become steadily more attentive and less restless as they mature. Usually they can concentrate well enough for all practical purposes by the time they leave school. In this sense, the reassurance that 'he will grow out of it' is well founded – at least for the majority. On the other hand, it can leave behind serious scars.

If a child becomes unpopular, lonely and a failure at school then those complications will not necessarily disappear when the core problems improve. Parents and teachers can be helpful in reducing these complications, and in so doing make the final outcome better (see Chapters five, eight and ten).

Is hyperactivity a physical illness?

No; there are many causes. Several physical illnesses can cause children to lose concentration or behave badly. The most important, and commonest, is probably unrecognized deafness. However, the majority of hyperactive children do not have any known physical disease (see Chapters three and six).

But isn't hyperactivity the result of brain damage?

Not usually. Brain damage can cause children to be hyperactive, or to show other psychological problems; but the great majority of hyperactive children do not have damaged brains. Many do have an immaturity of some particular aspect of psychological development (see Chapter three); and it is possible that future research will find this to be based on slow development of parts of the brain. If so, the likely causes are the interactions between the characteristics a child inherits and the environment he encounters. Most injuries to the brain have only a weak effect upon subsequent personality development.

The terms 'minimal brain damage' and 'MBD' can be very confusing. Some paediatricians and psychiatrists used to use the phrase as another word for hyperactivity or attention deficit, whatever the cause. If the phrase is used nowadays, it will probably be because a physician thinks that something has affected normal brain development in a particular child. It is definitely worth discussing what the damage is likely to have been.

Can girls be hyperactive?

Certainly, but boys are three or four times more likely to be diagnosed as hyperactive. Girls are less vulnerable, but if they do become affected, they are then just as likely to need help as boys with hyperactivity.

Is hyperactivity the same as dyslexia?

Poor concentration can be one kind of slow development. The inability to learn to read can result from it, but is more often due to other kinds of slow development (for example, in language or recognizing shapes). Many hyperactive children find it harder than other children to learn to read. But most children with reading problems start to become increasingly restless and disruptive as their school career proceeds, because of their difficulties in coping with academic work. In other words, hyperactivity can cause reading problems, and reading problems can make children restless and inattentive, but the two sorts of problems are essentially separate (see Chapter four).

Is hyperactivity the fault of the parents?

In a word, no. Most parents feel responsible and guilty for the difficulties of their children. In practice, however, neither child nor parent is usually to blame. Sometimes a vicious cycle develops in which both make matters worse; both are victims. But nearly always, parents can help their children's development. Chapters seven and eight go into some practical self-help steps that do not necessarily require professional supervision. Nevertheless, professional help should be available when things can no longer be sorted out simply (see Chapter nine).

Are diets the answer?

A few children can indeed be helped by ridding their normal diet of foodstuffs to which they are sensitive. On the other hand, scientific studies (and my own experience) suggest that such children are very much in a minority. It is more common for a diet to help only for a few days or weeks; this is often because of the psychological boost of starting a new treatment.

I do not myself advise the majority of families to start a diet treatment. But it is reasonable for parents to decide for themselves providing they understand that it may very well not help. Furthermore, one should not become discouraged if diets do not work. This is, in a sense, expected, and there are many other kinds of treatment to try. Diets are most likely to help children who are already known to have a physical allergy to foods (such as a skin rash), or to suffer from food-related headaches (see Chapter six).

Do hyperactive children have to be drugged?

Psychotherapy and behaviour modification treatments are becoming increasingly available, and correspondingly drug treatments are used to a lesser extent (see Chapter nine). Some drug treatments, however, especially stimulants, are still very useful in helping the more severely affected children to respond to education or treatment. It is better to think of such treatments as 'medicine' rather than as 'drugs'.

Their purpose is not to tranquillize, nor to subtract something from the child's behaviour, nor to cheer the child up artificially. Rather, they help a child to focus on an activity and to sustain concentration. They can therefore be useful in tiding children over a period of developmental delay until their abilities are maturing naturally. They only *allow* children to focus and control themselves, not *make* them do so. People taking such tablets should therefore not regard them as an alibi or a complete answer. Medical treatment in this context is a support, not a cure.

What can be done more widely to make life better for hyperactive children?

Parents' self-help groups should be important routes for increasing knowledge and understanding. In Britain at least, there is probably a need for more public and professional recognition of the condition, and again voluntary bodies ought to be helpful in this. It is equally important that we do not focus too much attention on hyperactivity, because then all kinds of psychological stress can be neglected simply because a useful label has been attached to the child.

Sometimes voluntary groups can get preoccupied with one treatment (such as diet) and this too can get in the way of a wider educating role. Teachers should give some priority to working out and assessing better ways of teaching hyperactive children at different stages of their development. Research also needs to be supported. There is a scientific argument about most of the issues that have been raised in this book. The arguments need to be resolved before people can start to help in a coordinated way.

This book has put a personal view precisely because so many people are now confused by the controversies. I hope that it will also have emphasized how much we need better information if we are to improve the lives of unfortunate children whose psychological development is clouded by hyperkinesis.

Appendix

Research diagnostic criteria

The research diagnosis of hyperkinetic disorder requires the definite presence of abnormal levels of inattention and over-activity/impulsiveness that are pervasive across situations and persistent over time and that are not caused by other disorders such as autism or affective disorders. All the following need to be present:

1. **Inattention**: At least six of the following symptoms of inattention have persisted for at least six months to a degree that is maladaptive and inconsistent with developmental level:

   (a) often fails to give close attention to details or makes careless mistakes in schoolwork, work, or other activities.
   (b) often fails to sustain attention in tasks or play activities.
   (c) often does not seem to listen to what is being said to him or her.
   (d) often does not follow through on instructions and fails to finish schoolwork, chores, or duties in the workplace (not due to oppositional behaviour or failure to understand instructions).
   (e) often is impaired in organizing tasks and activities.
   (f) often avoids or strongly dislikes tasks (such as schoolwork or homework) that require sustained mental effort.
   (g) often loses things necessary for tasks or activities (e.g. school assignments, pencils, books, tools, or toys).

(h) is often easily distracted by extraneous stimuli.
(i) often forgetful in daily activities.

2. **Hyperactivity-Impulsivity:** At least four of the following symptoms of hyperactivity-impulsivity have persisted for at least six months to a degree that is maladaptive and inconsistent with developmental level:
   (a) often fidgets with hands or feet or squirms in seat.
   (b) leaves seat in classroom or in other situations in which remaining seated is expected.
   (c) often runs about or climbs excessively in situations where it is inappropriate (in adolescents or adults, may be limited to subjective feelings of restlessness).
   (d) often is unduly noisy in playing or does not engage in leisure activities quietly.

   Impulsivity
   (e) often blurts out answers to questions before the questions have been completed
   (f) often fails to wait in lines or await turn in games or group situations.

3. Onset no later than seven years of age.

4. **Pervasiveness:** Criteria should be met for more than a single situation, e.g. the combination of inattention and overactivity should be present both at home and at school, or at both school and another setting where children are observed, such as a clinic. *Note* evidence for cross-situationality will ordinarily require information from more than one source: parental report about classroom behaviour, for instance, is unlikely to be sufficient.

5. The disturbance causes clinically significant distress or impairment in social, academic, or occupational functioning.

6. Does not meet criteria for pervasive developmental disorder, mania, depressive or anxiety disorder.

Many authorities also recognize conditions that are subthreshold for hyperkinetic disorder. Children who meet criteria in other ways but do not show abnormalities of overactivity/impulsiveness may be recognized as showing *attention deficit*; conversely, children falling short of criteria on attention problems but meeting criteria in other respects may be recognized as *activity disorder*. In the same way, children who meet criteria for only one situation (e.g. at home only) may be regarded as showing a *home-specific* or *classroom-specific disorder*. These conditions are not yet included in the main classification because of insufficient empirical predictive validation, and because many children with subthreshold disorders show other syndromes (such as oppositional disorder) and should be classified there.

Useful addresses

LADDER (Learning, Hyperactivity and Attention Deficit Disorders Association)
P.O. Box 700
Wolverhampton WV3 7YY
(please enclose an SAE) tel: 0902 336272

Action Against Allergy
43 The Downs
London SW20 8HG

Association for Children with Learning Difficulties
Quirral House
Pitch Place
Thursley
Godalming
Surrey

British Epilepsy Association
Anstey House
40 Hanover Square
Leeds
Yorks LS3 1BE

British Institute for Brain Injured Children
Knowle Hall
Knowle, Bridgwater
Somerset

CALIP (*Campaign Against Lead in Petrol*)
63 Dora Road
London SW19 7HH

Camphill Rudolf Steiner School (Central Office)
Murtle House
Bieldside
Aberdeen

CLEAR (*The Campaign for Lead Free Air*)
2 Northdown Street
London N1 9BG

Food Allergy Association
c/o The Chairman
Mrs Ellen Rothera
27 Ferringham Lane
Ferring
West Sussex BN12 5NB

Hyperactive Children's Support Group
71 Whyke Lane
Chichester
West Sussex PO19 2LD

National Children's Bureau
8 Wakley Street
Islington
London EC1V 7QE

National Society for Prevention of Cruelty to Children
67 Saffron Hill
London EC1N 8RS
tel: 071-242 1626

Royal Society for mentally handicapped children and adults (MENCAP)
123 Golden Lane
London EC1 0RT

Spastic Society
12 Park Crescent
London W1N 4EQ

CANADA

Canadian Institute of Child Health
17 York Street
Suite 202
Ottawa
Ontario K1N 5S7

Canadian Paediatric Society
Centre hospitalier universitaire de Sherbrooke
Sherbrooke
Quebec J1H 5N4

Human Nutrition Research Council of Ontario
PO Box 38
Stittsville
Ontario K0A 3G0

Society for Emotionally Disturbed Children
1622 Sherbrooke Street West
3rd Floor
Montreal
Quebec H3H 1C9

AUSTRALIA

Active Hyperkinetic Children's Association
PO Box 17
East Doncaster
Victoria 3109

Hyperactivity Association of NSW
24/29 Bertram Street
Chatswood NSW 2067

Hyperactivity Association of South Australia Inc
18 King William Road
North Adelaide SA 5006

Hyperactive Help (WA)
88 Manning Street
Scarborough WA 6019

Launceston Hyperactivity Association
Mrs P. Motton
C/- PO
Meander
Tasmania 7304

Mackay Hyperactivity Association
PO Box 204
Mackay
Queensland 4740

Queensland Hyperactivity Association
PO Box 107
Veronga
Queensland 4104

NEW ZEALAND

Auckland Hyperactivity Association Inc
PO Box 36-099
Northcote
Auckland NZ

Waikato Hyperkinetic Children's Support Group
C/- 10 McFarlane Street
Hamilton NZ

Wellington Hyperactivity and Allergy Association Inc
93 Waipapa Road
Hataitai
Wellington NZ

Further reading

There are several textbooks that are intended for professionals, but can still be of interest to anyone who wants to study the subject in depth. I have edited one of them: Taylor E.A. (Ed.) *The Overactive Child. Clinics in Developmental Medicine No. 97.* Blackwell Scientific Publications, Oxford, 1986. I can also recommend Prior M. & Griffin M. *Hyperactivity: Diagnosis and management.* Heinemann Medical Books, London, 1985, and Goldstein S. and Goldstein M. *Managing Attention Disorders in Children.* Wiley, New York, 1990.

The question of diet will loom large in many readers' minds. The research scene is changing fast, but one book written to explain the scientific issues to a non-professional audience is still useful: Conners C.K. *Food Additives and Hyperactive Children.* Plenum Press, New York, 1980. Serfontein G. *The Hidden Handicap,* Simon & Schuster, Australia, is an account of hyperactivity written for parents that many find useful.

There are several practical manuals about how parents can apply behaviour modification to children's behaviour problems. Two good ones are *Living with Children* by Gerald Patterson and M. Elizabeth Gullion, and *Parents are Teachers* by Wesley C. Becker. Both are published by Research Press, Champaign, Illinois. A very good Penguin book describes both the behaviour modification approach and many other aspects of childhood hyperactivity: *Is my Child Hyperactive?* Jo Douglas, Penguin Books, 1991.

Acknowledgements

I am greatly indebted to Catherine Buckley for her help with the organization and presentation of this book. More generally, I am glad to acknowledge the contribution of my patients, their families and my colleagues – from whom I have learned everything that is accurate in these pages.

Eric Taylor 1985

The publishers would like to thank the following individuals and organizations for their help in the production of this book:
Sally & Richard Greenhill for the photographs on pages 35, 82 and 98; Camilla Jessel, FRPS for the photographs on page 18; Pictor International for the photograph on page 48; Vision International/ Anthea Sieveking for the photograph on page 13.

Our thanks to David Gifford for drawing the diagrams and to Jennifer Eaton for compiling the drug tables.

International drug-name equivalents

Generic name	UK trade name	Canada trade name	US trade name	Australia trade name
amphetamine	Durophet*	Benzedrine	Obetrol*	not available
chlordiazepoxide	Librium Tropium	Librium Solium etc	Librium A-Poxide	Librium
chlorpromazine	Largactil	Largactil	Thorazine	Largactil Protran
dexamphetamine	Dexedrine Durophet*			See note 3
dextroamphetamine	see dexamphetamine	Dexedrine	Dexedrine Obetrol*	
diazepam	Valium Tensium Solis Atensine etc	Valium Meval Rival E-pam etc	Valium	Valium Ducene Pro-Pam
haloperidol	Serenace Haldol Fortunan	Peridol Haldol etc	Haldol	Serenace Pacedol
methylphenidate	Ritalin	Ritalin	Ritalin	Ritalin
pemoline	Ronyl Volital	not available	Cylert	not available
penicillamine	Distamine Pendramine	Cuprimine Depen	Cuprimine Depen	D-Penamine Perdolat

Key: *denotes that drug is in combination with one or more other active ingredients.

Notes
1. The trade names listed apply to the oral solid dosage form (i.e. tablet or capsule) of the drug.
2. Some drugs are marketed under many trade names. In some cases only a few of the trade names have been listed; the presence of further trade names is indicated by 'etc.'
3. Dexamphetamine is marketed in Australia as an unbranded product only.

Index

Page numbers in *italic* refer to illustrations

'A-B-C' scheme, 97
accidents, 86
active children, 2
'active ignoring', 70–71, 75, 80, 83
activity, learning control of, 74–7
ADD (Attention Deficit Disorder), vii, viii,
    ix, x, xi, xiii, xiv
ADHD (Attention Deficit Hyperactive
    Disorder), ix, xi, xiii, xiv
additives, food, 56–7, 58–60, 61–2
adolescence, 102
aggressive behaviour, 4, 41, 49, 99, 101
    tantrums, 83–4
    television violence, 85
alcohol, in pregnancy, 26
alienation, 101, 102
allergic reactions, 32, 56–7
    to food, 56–65, 109
amphetamines, 8, 92–5
antenatal care, 26
antisocial behaviour, 4, 41–2, 49, 99
arguments, parental, 51–2
art therapists, 90
artificial colours, in food, 56, 59, 61–3
ascorbic acid, 64
assessment, 88–9, 97, 99
asthma, 57, 61
attention,
    attention span, 20
    learning to organize, 53
    parental, 70
    parent's withdrawal of, 70–71, 75, 80,
        83
    problems in school, 36–40
Attention Deficit Disorder (ADD), vii, viii,
    ix, x, xi, xiii, xiv, 4, 5, 107
Attention Deficit Hyperactive Disorder
    (ADHD), ix, xi, xiii, xiv
audiologists, 90

bargaining, 74
Barkley, Professor Russell, ix
battered children, 49, 86–7
bedtime problems, 79–80
bedtime rituals, 80
behaviour disorders, 89
behaviour modification, 44, 89, 97–8,
    109
biological causes, 22–31
birth, brain damage during, 26–7
boredom, 2, 85
boys, hyperactivity, 24, 108
brain,
    damage at birth, 26–7, 32, 107–8
    effects of stimulants on, 91–2; *93*
    imaging, 27
    injuries, 26–7, 32, 107–8
    lead poisoning, 28–9
    minimal brain damage, 4, 5, 107–8
    research, 104
bribery, 69–70

caffeine, 60–61
care, children in, 89
CHADD (Children and Adults with ADD) ,
    ix
child battering, 49, 86–7
Child Development Centre, xii
child guidance units, 87
child psychiatrists, 88–9
Children and Adults with ADD (CHADD),
    ix
children's homes, 53–4, 103
chlordiazepoxide, 91–2
chlorpromazine, 92
chromosomes, 22
clinical psychologists, 89, 97
clinics, 88–100
communication, language development, 25,
    32, 40, 81, 108
    through tantrums, 81–4
computers, teaching aids, 85

concentration,
    attention problems, 38–40
    learning control of, 53, 74–6
    poor, 4, 12
conduct disorder, 4
confidentiality, clinics, 90–91
conflict, cycle of, 49; 50
consistency, parental behaviour, 71
control,
    behaviour therapy, 97–8
    child's loss of, 82–3
    parent's loss of, 76
    self-control, 2–3, 74
counselling, 87, 89

dark, fear of, 78
day centres, 102
day nurseries, 85
deafness, 12, 32, 90, 107
delinquency, 9, 101
dependence, 84
deprived homes, 53–4
development,
    rate of, 74
    slow, 24–5, 32–3, 107–8
dextroamphetamine, 91
diary, keeping of, 55
diazepam, 91
diet, 18, 55–65, 96, 109
    deficiences, 57
    exclusion diets, 55, 57, 60–63
    food allergy, 56–65, 109
dietitians, 90
'difficult' children, 21
discipline, 41, 49, 54, 66–7, 71
doctors, xii, 87, 91
dopamine, 92
drama therapists, 90
drug addiction, 93–4
drugs,
    amphetamines, 8, 92–4
    hypnotics, 79, 81
    and lead poisoning, 29–30
    method of working, 92–3; 93
    neuroleptics, 92
    risks, 93–5
    safety, 86, 94
    stimulants, 8, 81, 91–4, 109; 93
    tranquillizers, 91–2
    treatment with, 6–7, 8, 91–6, 109; 93
dyslexia, 108

ear infections, 32
education, xi–xii,
    'Children with Special Needs', xii
educational psychologists, 37, 44, 89, 97

eggs, allergy to, 57
electricity, safety, 86
erythrosine, 56
evening primrose oil, viii, 56
exclusion diets, 55, 57, 60–63

families,
    coping with hyperactivity, 66–76, 102–3,
        107–8
    family therapy, 89, 99–100
    parent-child relationships, 21, 46–54
fatty acids, 56
fear,
    of the dark, 78
    of loneliness, 78, 80
Feingold diet, 56–7, 58–60, 61–2, 63–4
fetal alcohol syndrome, 26
food,
    additives, 56–7, 58–9, 61
    allergic reactions to, 55–65, 109
    artificial colours, 56, 59, 61–2
    exclusion diets, 55, 57, 60–63
    preservatives, 56
    salicylates, 56, 62
friendships, 43–4
fruit,
    Feingold diet, 63
    salicylates, 56, 62
frustration, 102
functional analysis, 97

genes, 22
genetics, 22, 23
girls, hyperactivity, 24, 108
goals, 74–6
'good conduct report system', 42, 68, 72;
    43, 69, 70

haloperidol, 92
head injuries, 27
headaches, 32, 94, 109
health visitors, 87, 91
hearing problems, 12, 32, 90, 107
heredity, 22; 23
high activity, definition, 3
home, safety in, 86
hormones, in pregnancy, 26
hospitals,
    long-term, 103
    paediatrics departments, 87
hostels, 53–4, 103
hyperactivity,
    causes, 107
    characteristics, 1–3, 106–7
    complications, 9, 66–77, 78–87
    diagnosis, 8–9, 10–21, 47–9

diet and, 55–65
duration, 106
extent of problem, 7–8
family reactions to, 49–54
family relationships, 46–54
impulsivity, 112
living with, 66–77, 101–5, 108
as a myth, 6–7
physical causes, 17–33
recognizing, 36–7
in school, 34–45
sex differences, 24, 108
terminology, 3–4
treatment, 8–9, 88–100
hyperkinetic syndrome, vii, 3, 4, 68
hypnotic medicines, 79, 81

illness, 32–3
immaturity, 53, 84, 107
immune system, food allergy, 57
inattention, 111–12
inconsistency, parental, 51–2, 71
independence, 74, 84–5, 102–3
inheritance, 22; 23
institutional care, 53–4, 103
intensive remedial teaching, 44
IQ tests, 40, 89

LADDER (Learning Hyperactivity and
    Attention Deficit Disorders
    Association, vii, x, xiii, xiv
language development, 25, 32, 40, 81, 108
lead poisoning, 28–31; 30
learning disorders, 4, 12, 40, 89, 101–2
Learning, Hyperactivity and Attention
    Deficit Disorders Association
    (LADDER), vii, x, xiii, xiv
letting off steam, 73
local authority, children in care, 89–90
loneliness, and sleep problems, 78, 80

'major tranquillizers', 92
male hormones, in pregnancy, 26
maturity, 74, 84, 95, 102–3
MBD, 4, 107–8
medicines see drugs
megavitamin therapy, 57
mental illness, 102
methylphenidate, 8, 91
microcomputers, teaching aids, 85
milk, allergy to, 57
minerals, diet deficiency, viii, 57
minimal brain damage, 4, 5, 107–8
minimal brain dysfunction, 4
Mould, Stan, vii–xiv

nerve cells, 92
neuroleptics, 92
night terrors, 80
night waking, 80
nightmares, 80
noradrenaline, 92
nurseries, 37, 85
nurses, 90

occupational therapists, 90
oligoantigenic diets, 57
orphanages, 53–4
overactivity, 7, 15, 106
    and age of child, 19–20
    definition, 3

paediatricians, 90, 91
paediatric departments, 87
parents,
    attention to child, 70
    child battering, 86
    coping with hyperactivity, 66–77, 103,
        108
    encouraging child's independence, 84–5
    loss of self-control, 76
    parental anger, 68
    parent–child relationships, 21, 46–54
    withdrawal of attention, 70, 75, 80, 83
pemoline, 91
penicillamine, 29
personality disorders, 9
pervasiveness, 112–13
physical causes, 17–33
physical illness, 32–3
physical treatments, 91–5
placebo effect, 58
play
    and boredom, 85
    rituals, 85
playgroups, 37, 85
praise, as reward, 75–6
pre-eclampsia, 26
pregnancy, 26–7
preservatives, in food, 56
professional advice, 87, 88–100, 101, 108,
    110
prostaglandins, 56
psychiatric clinics, 91
psychiatrists, 88–9, 97
psychological services, xii
psychological testing, 88–9
psychologists,
    child, 89
    clinical, 97
    educational, 44, 89, 97
psychotherapy, 89, 95, 99–100, 109; 98

puberty, 102
punishment, 49, 54, 70, 98
pyridoxine, diet deficiency, 57

rages, 81–4; *82*
rashes, 57, 61, 109
reading problems, 108
remedial teaching, 39–40, 44, 90
research, 104–5, 110
  diagnostic criteria, 111–13
rewards, 68–70, 71, 75–6, 98; *77*
Ritalin, x
rituals,
  bedtime, 80
  play, 85
rules, social, 71, 98

safety, 86, 94
salicylates, 56, 62
scapegoats, 47
schools, xii, 34–45, 102
  special schools, 44–5
self-control, 2, 74, 98
self-help groups, 101–2, 110
separation from parents, 36
Serfontein, Dr Gordon, *The Hidden
  Handicap*, viii
sex differences, 24, 108
skin rashes, 57, 61, 109
sleep, length of, 81
sleep problems, 78–81, 94
sleeping drugs, 79, 81
slow development, 24–5, 32–3, 107–8
slow learners, 25
smoking, 26
social learning, 71, 81, 98
social workers, 87, 89, 91, 97
sodium glutamate, 56
soft drinks, caffeine content, 60–61
special schools, 44–5
specialized clinics, 88–91
speech therapists, 90
star charts, 75; *77*
stealing, 41
stimulants, 8, 81, 91–3, 109; *93*

stress, 2, 15
  and night waking, 80
  parental, 47
  tantrums, 21, 80, 81–4; *82*
tartrazine, 56
teachers, 90, 110
television, 85
temperament, 19–21, 32
therapy,
  behaviour modification, 44, 89, 95,
    97–8, 109
  family therapy, 89, 99
  future prospects, 104
  psychotherapy, 89, 95, 99, 109; *98*
  speech therapy, 90
toddlers, tantrums, 81
toxaemia, 26
toys, boredom with, 85
tranquillizers, 91
treatment, 88–100
  behaviour modification, 44, 89, 95,
    97–8, 109
  clinics, 90–91
  drug, 6–7, 8, 91–6, 109; *93*
  physical, 91–6
  psychotherapy, 99–100; *98*
truancy, 41
twins, 22; *23*
tyranny, 50–51

video games, 85
videotape recordings, clinic interviews, 90
violence,
  child battering, 86–7
  tantrums, 83–4
  on television, 85
vitamins,
  diet deficiency, viii, 57
  Feingold diet, 63
voluntary help organizations, 87, 110,
  114–18

wheat, allergy to, 57

zinc, diet deficiency, viii, 57

Other books in the Positive Health Guide series

CHILDREN'S PROBLEMS
A parents' guide to understanding and tackling them
Dr Bryan Lask

THE ALLERGY DIET
How to overcome your food intolerance
Elizabeth Workman, SRD, Dr John Hunter and
Dr Virginia Alun Jones

THE DIABETICS' DIET BOOK
A new high-fibre eating programme
Dr Jim Mann and the Oxford Dietetic Group

ECZEMA AND DERMATITIS
How to cope with inflamed skin
Prof Rona MacKie

ANXIETY AND DEPRESSION
A practical guide to recovery
Prof Robert Priest

ACNE
Advice on clearing your skin
Prof Ronald Marks

OVERCOMING DYSLEXIA
A straightforward guide for families and teachers
Dr Bevé Hornsby

ASTHMA AND HAY FEVER
How to relieve wheezing and sneezing
Dr Allan Knight

STRESS AND RELAXATION
Self-help ways to cope with stress and relieve nervous tension, ulcers, insomnia, migraine and high blood pressure
Jane Madders

VARICOSE VEINS
How they are treated, and what you can do to help
Prof Harold Ellis

GET A BETTER NIGHT'S SLEEP
Prof Ian Oswald and Dr Kirstine Adam

MIGRAINE AND HEADACHES
Dr Marcia Wilkinson

THE BACK – RELIEF FROM PAIN
Patterns of back pain – how to deal with and avoid them
Dr Alan Stoddard

[ ] CHILDREN'S PROBLEMS by Dr Bryan Lask	£6.99
[ ] THE ALLERGY DIET by Dr Hunter, Dr Jones and E. Workman	£5.99
[ ] THE DIABETIC'S DIET BOOK by Dr J. Mann	£4.99
[ ] ECZEMA AND DERMATITIS by Prof R. Mackie	£5.99
[ ] ANXIETY AND DEPRESSION by Prof R. Priest	£7.99
[ ] ACNE by Prof R. Marks	£4.99
[ ] OVERCOMING DYSLEXIA by Dr B. Hornsby	£7.99
[ ] ASTHMA AND HAY FEVER by Dr A. Knight	£6.99
[ ] STRESS AND RELAXATION by J. Madders	£7.99
[ ] VARICOSE VEINS by Prof. H. Ellis	£6.99
[ ] GET A BETTER NIGHT'S SLEEP by Prof I. Oswald & Dr K. Adam	£5.99
[ ] MIGRAINE AND HEADACHES by Dr M. Wilkinson	£6.99

Optima Books now offers an exciting range of quality titles by both established and new authors which can be ordered from the following address:

Little, Brown and Company (UK) Limited,
PO Box 11, Falmouth, Cornwall TR10 9EN
Alternatively, you may fax your order to the above address.
Fax No. 071 412 8100

Payments can be made as follows: cheque, postal order (payable to Little, Brown and Company) or by credit cards, Visa/Access. Do not send cash or currency. UK customers and B.F.P.O. please allow £1.00 for postage and packing for the first book, plus 50p for the second book, plus 30p for each additional book up to a maximum charge of £3.00 (7 books plus).

Overseas customers including Ireland please allow £2.00 for the first book, plus £1.00 for the second book, plus 50p for each additional book.

NAME (Block letters) ....

....

ADDRESS ....

....

....

☐ I enclose my remittance for £ ....

☐ I wish to pay by Access/Visa card

Number ....

Card Expiry Date ....